ADAPTING TO CLIMATE CHANGE: NATIONAL STRATEGY AND PROGRESS

CLIMATE CHANGE AND ITS CAUSES, EFFECTS AND PREDICTION

Additional books in this series can be found on Nova's website under the Series tab.

Additional E-books in this series can be found on Nova's website under the E-book tab.

ENVIRONMENTAL SCIENCE, ENGINEERING AND TECHNOLOGY

Additional books in this series can be found on Nova's website under the Series tab.

Additional E-books in this series can be found on Nova's website under the E-book tab.

CLIMATE CHANGE AND ITS CAUSES, EFFECTS AND PREDICTION

ADAPTING TO CLIMATE CHANGE: NATIONAL STRATEGY AND PROGRESS

GERARD ROBINSON

AND

LILLIAN K. MOORE

EDITORS

Nova Science Publishers, Inc.

New York

Library of Congress Cataloging-in-Publication Data

Adapting to climate change : national strategy and progress / editors, Gerard Robinson and Lillian K. Moore.
    p. cm.
  Includes index.
  ISBN 978-1-61942-749-5 (hardcover)
  1. Climatic changes--Risk management--Government policy--United States. 2. Regional planning--United States. I. Robinson, Gerard, 1969- II. Moore, Lillian K.
  QC903.2.U6A32 2011
  363.738'745610973--dc23
                          2011052165

Published by Nova Science Publishers, Inc. † New York

CONTENTS

PREFACE

As concentrations of greenhouse gases and heat-trapping particles increase in the atmosphere, it is becoming ever more urgent to understand and prepare for the resulting changes in climate. These changes include not only temperature increases but also shifts in precipitation patterns, storm tracks, and other parameters. Climate change affects human health, water and energy supplies, food production, coastal communities, ecosystems, and many other aspects of society and the environment. This book presents an overview of the national strategy and progress that the federal government is taking in adapting to climate change with a focus on the progress report of the Interagency Climate Change Adaptation Task Force.

Chapter 1- As concentrations of greenhouse gases and heat-trapping particles increase in the atmosphere, it is becoming ever more urgent to understand and prepare for the resulting changes in climate. These changes include not only temperature increases but also shifts in precipitation patterns, storm tracks, and other parameters. Climate change affects human health, water and energy supplies, food production, coastal communities, ecosystems, and many other aspects of society and the environment. The Obama Administration is committed to reducing greenhouse gas emissions to minimize the impacts of climate change. But mitigation alone is not enough. People are already feeling the impacts of climate change and future changes are inevitable. To prepare and respond to these impacts, the Administration is also committed to climate change adaptation.

Chapter 2- In October 2009, President Obama signed Executive Order 13514, *Federal Leadership in Environmental and Energy Performance*, which sets sustainability goals for federal agencies and focuses on making improvements in agency environmental, energy, and economic performance.

The Executive Order charged the Interagency Climate Change Adaptation Task Force with providing recommendations on how federal policies, programs, and planning efforts can better prepare the United States for climate change. In October 2010, the task force recommended a set of policy goals and actions in its Progress Report to the president. The task force outlined how the Federal Government should work with local, state, and tribal partners to provide leadership, coordination, science, and services to address climate risks to the nation as well as federal assets and operations. In the 2010 Report, the task force committed to providing an update on federal government adaptation progress in 2011. This report provides that update in five key adaptation areas that align with the policy goals set forth by the task force in 2010:

In: Adapting to Climate Change ISBN: 978-1- 61942-749-5
Editors: G. Robinson and L. K. Moore © 2012 Nova Science Publishers, Inc

Chapter 1

PROGRESS REPORT OF THE INTERAGENCY CLIMATE CHANGE ADAPTATION TASK FORCE[*]

The White House Council on Environmental Quality

LIST OF ACRONYMS

CDC	Centers for Disease Control
CEQ	Council on Environmental Quality
DHS	Department of Homeland Security
DOE	Department of Energy
DOI	Department of the Interior
DOT	Department of Transportation
EPA	Environmental Protection Agency
FEMA	Federal Emergency Management Agency
FHWA	Federal Highway Administration
HHS	Department of Health and Human Services
HUD	Department of Housing and Urban Development
IPCC	Intergovernmental Panel on Climate Change

---

[*] This is an edited, reformatted and augmented version of the Progress Report of the Interagency Climate Change Adaptation Task Force, The White House Council on Environmental Quality, dated October 5, 2010.

GAO	Government Accountability Office
MCC	Millennium Challenge Corporation
NASA	National Aeronautics and Space Administration
NCA	National Climate Assessment
NFIP	National Flood Insurance Program
NFWPCAS	National Fish, Wildlife and Plants Climate Adaptation Strategy
NGO Non	Non-Governmental Organization
NOAA	National Oceanic and Atmospheric Administration
OFEE	Office of the Federal Environmental Executive
OMB	Office of Management and Budget
OSTP	Office of Science and Technology Policy
Task Force	Interagency Climate Change Adaptation Task Force
UNDP	United Nations Development Programme
UNEP	United Nations Environment Programme
UNFCCC	United Nations Framework Convention on Climate Change
USACE	U.S. Army Corps of Engineers
USAID	U.S. Agency for International Development
USDA	U.S. Department of Agriculture
USFWS	U.S. Fish and Wildlife Service
USGCRP	U.S. Global Change Research Program
USGS	U.S. Geological Survey

We envision a resilient, healthy, and prosperous nation in the face of a changing climate.

EXECUTIVE SUMMARY

As concentrations of greenhouse gases and heat-trapping particles increase in the atmosphere, it is becoming ever more urgent to understand and prepare for the resulting changes in climate. These changes include not only temperature increases but also shifts in precipitation patterns, storm tracks, and other parameters. Climate change affects human health, water and energy supplies, food production, coastal communities, ecosystems, and many other aspects of society and the environment. The Obama Administration is committed to reducing greenhouse gas emissions to minimize the impacts of climate change. But mitigation alone is not enough. People are already feeling the impacts of climate change and future changes are inevitable. To prepare and respond to these impacts, the Administration is also committed to climate change adaptation.

The scope, severity, and pace of future climate change impacts are difficult to predict. However, observations and long-term scientific trends indicate that the potential impacts of a changing climate on society and the environment will be significant. Projected impacts include more frequent heat waves and high-intensity precipitation events, rising sea levels, ocean acidification, and more prolonged droughts. The year-round average air temperature in the United States has already risen by more than 2°F over the past 50 years and is projected to increase further in the future.[1] On average, wet areas of the United States will become wetter and dry areas will become drier. Adding to the challenge of responding to these impacts, climate-related changes do not act in isolation but rather interact with and often exacerbate the impacts of other non-climatic stressors such as habitat destruction, overharvesting, and pollution.

Climate change is a global phenomenon that is influenced by and affects people and places throughout the world. Vulnerability to climate change differs across countries, communities, and even households. For instance, shoreline communities, socially or economically disadvantaged populations, as well as sensitive ecosystems such as coral reefs, wetlands, and Arctic habitats, are generally more vulnerable to climate impacts.

Coastal areas will need to prepare for rising sea levels and increased flooding.

Understanding and preparing for climate change requires both domestic and international action. Adapting to climate change involves actions by individuals, businesses, governments, and others to build resilience and reduce vulnerability of human and natural systems to unavoidable climate impacts. Adaptation also reduces the long-term costs of responding to these impacts. Adaptation measures should focus on helping the most vulnerable people and places reduce their exposure and sensitivity to climate change and improve their capacity to predict, prepare for, and avoid adverse impacts. This requires thoughtful planning, continued investment in science and analytical tools, and the development of practical, cost-effective measures and technologies for adapting to future climate conditions.

Local impacts from climate change, such as crop loss or severe flooding, often have consequences that extend beyond regional or even national borders – for example, changes in human migration and disruptions in food supply. Climate change has direct implications for United States foreign assistance, national security, and diplomatic interests, including the considerable resources that the United States dedicates to disaster response and humanitarian assistance overseas. Moreover, the United States is a major contributor to, and beneficiary of, the global science and technology development community. The United States should continue to engage with international partners to enhance our understanding of climate change and leverage collective knowledge and resources.

The Role of the Federal Government in Adapting to Climate Change

The federal government has an important and unique role in climate adaptation, but it is only one part of a broader effort that must include multiple levels of government and private and non-governmental partners throughout the country. In particular, Federal leadership, guidance, information, and support are vital to planning for and implementing adaptive actions. Because climate impacts span political boundaries, the federal government must respond in partnership with communities, Tribes, and states – many of which are already beginning to implement adaptation measures. Effective adaptation requires that stakeholders in affected regions coordinate their responses to climate impacts on shared infrastructure and resources.

The federal government has an important stake in adaptation because climate change directly affects Federal lands, including National Parks and forests.

At the core of the federal government's role should be a commitment to promote and implement best practices for adaptation, build greater public awareness and understanding of the importance of adaptation, and maintain dialogue and partnerships with stakeholders and decision makers. The Government should continue to enhance services that enable informed decisions based on the best available science, and to work with the international community to improve knowledge sharing and coordinate adaptation investments. The Government should also consider how Federal policies may lead to unintended consequences that increase the nation's vulnerability to climate risks, thus making adaptation more costly and difficult. For example, certain policies may lead to increased development in the very areas that climate risks would suggest people avoid.

The federal government also has an important stake in adaptation because climate change directly affects a wide range of Federal services, operations, programs, assets (e.g., infrastructure, land), and our national security. The Government must exercise a leadership role to address climate impacts on Federal infrastructure interests and on natural, cultural, and historic resources that it has statutory responsibilities to protect. The federal government should identify its most significant adaptation risks and opportunities and incorporate response strategies into its planning to ensure that Federal resources are invested wisely and that its services and operations remain effective in the context of a changing climate. Importantly, the federal government must work in partnership with local, state, Tribal, and regional authorities as it develops and implements adaptation strategies, since most adaptive actions will occur at the local level.

The Interagency Climate Change Adaptation Task Force

The Interagency Climate Change Adaptation Task Force (Task Force) began meeting in Spring 2009. The Task Force is co-chaired by the Council on Environmental Quality (CEQ), the National Oceanic and Atmospheric Administration (NOAA), and the Office of Science and Technology Policy (OSTP). Recognizing the important role of the federal government in adaptation, President Obama signed an Executive Order on October 5, 2009 that called on the Task Force to recommend how the policies and practices of Federal agencies can be made compatible with and reinforce a national climate change adaptation strategy. The Executive Order charged the Task Force with delivering a report through the Chair of CEQ to the President within one year.

The Task Force, composed of more than 20 Federal agencies and Executive branch offices, formed workgroups to consider the capabilities of the federal government to respond to the impacts of climate change on select sectors, institutions, and agency responsibilities. The U.S. Global Change Research Program[2] (USGCRP) 2009 report, *Global Climate Change Impacts in the United States*, as well as other agency climate initiatives across the federal government, provided a basis for the work of the Task Force and its workgroups. In addition, the Task Force conducted numerous listening sessions and public outreach events with a wide range of stakeholders over the past year to gain greater perspective on how climate change is affecting our nation and what steps the federal government can take to foster a more coordinated and effective national response. Discussions were held with state, Tribal, regional, and local government officials, domestic and international non-governmental organizations (NGOs), scientists, academia, industry groups, and others. These discussions provided critical input to the Task Force as it developed the recommendations in this report.

Strategic Vision and Guiding Principles for Adaptation Policy and Actions

The work of the Task Force has been guided by a strategic vision of a resilient, healthy, and prosperous nation in the face of a changing climate. Achieving this vision will require innovative technology and ideas, as well as meaningful changes to policies, behavior, and institutions. It will also require a commitment to respond to climate change impacts that have already begun to occur while simultaneously taking proactive steps to understand and prepare for future climate conditions. To support these efforts, the Task Force has identified a set of guiding principles that should be considered by governments, communities, the private sector, and others in designing and implementing adaptation strategies.

GUIDING PRINCIPLES FOR ADAPTATION

Adopt Integrated Approaches: Adaptation should be incorporated into core policies, planning, practices, and programs whenever possible.

Prioritize the Most Vulnerable: Adaptation plans should prioritize helping people, places and infrastructure that are most vulnerable to climate impacts and be designed and implemented with meaningful involvement from all parts of society.

Use Best- Available Science: Adaptation should be grounded in the best- available scientific understanding of climate change risks, impacts, and vulnerabilities.

Build Strong Partnerships: Adaptation requires coordination across multiple sectors and scales and should build on the existing efforts and knowledge of a wide range of public and private stakeholders.

Apply Risk-Management Methods and Tools: Adaptation planning should incorporate risk- management methods and tools to help identify, assess, and prioritize options to reduce vulnerability to potential environmental, social, and economic implications of climate change.

Apply Ecosystem-based Approaches: Adaptation should, where relevant, take into account strategies to increase ecosystem resilience and protect critical ecosystem services on which humans depend to reduce vulnerability of human and natural systems to climate change.

Maximize Mutual Benefits: Adaptation should, where possible, use strategies that complement or directly support other related climate or environmental initiatives, such as efforts to improve disaster preparedness, promote sustainable resource management, and reduce greenhouse gas emissions including the development of cost- effective technologies.

> **Continuously Evaluate Performance:** Adaptation plans should include measureable goals and performance metrics to continuously assess whether adaptive actions are achieving desired outcomes.

Federal Policy Goals to Advance National Adaptation

The Task Force recommends that the federal government focus on a set of overarching goals that are consistent with the strategic vision and guiding principles. These policy goals are intended to reinforce existing adaptation efforts, harness a range of capabilities and resources across the federal government, and build strong partnerships with local, state, regional, Tribal, and international stakeholders to advance a common adaptation agenda.

Next Steps: Building a More Resilient Nation

The Task Force considers the recommendations in this report an initial set of priorities that the federal government should pursue to advance a national approach to adaptation. Implementing these actions will require the individual and collaborative efforts of Federal agencies. Agencies will initiate a formal adaptation planning process with the support of the Office of the Federal Environmental Executive (OFEE). USGCRP will continue efforts to build a robust body of science and critical tools to support decision making, and interagency workgroups will collaborate to address cross-cutting issues and support international adaptation objectives. In addition, agencies will continue to develop and strengthen individual and interagency adaptation initiatives, such as the National Climate Assessment and efforts to provide climate services (e.g., modeling, decision-support tools). The Task Force will continue to convene over the next year to support and oversee the implementation of these efforts and to establish a meaningful and sustained dialogue with partners at all levels of government. The Task Force will prepare another progress report in October 2011 that summarizes the results of implementation efforts and refines or expands recommended policy goals and actions where necessary.

The Task Force's work over the past year has increased awareness of climate change across the federal government and generated actions to address it. As the Government further integrates adaptation into its operations, policies and programs and provides guidance, and assistance, it will catalyze additional adaptation planning across the nation. The federal government will continue to develop a coordinated approach to adaptation by building partnerships with local, state, Tribal, private, and nonprofit stakeholders, many of whom already are playing a strong leadership role and implementing actions critical to a national adaptation strategy. Together, through the Federal actions described in this report and the collective action of stakeholders and government at all levels, we will strive to be a nation that better understands, and is better prepared for, the impacts of a changing climate.

SUMMARY OF POLICY GOALS AND RECOMMENDED ACTIONS FOR THE FEDERAL GOVERNMENT

1. **Encourage and Mainstream Adaptation Planning across the Federal Government** – *Climate change will challenge the mission, operations, and programs of nearly every Federal agency. Ensuring that the federal government has the capacity to execute its missions and maintain important services in the face of climate change is essential.*
   - Implement adaptation planning within Federal agencies
   - Employ a flexible framework for agency adaptation planning
   - Use a phased and coordinated approach to implement agency adaptation

2. **Improve Integration of Science into Decision Making** – *Access to integrated, interdisciplinary science is critical to understanding potential climate change impacts, and informing the development, implementation and evaluation of response strategies.*
   - Create a "roadmap" of existing Federal science efforts that inform and support adaptation
   - Prioritize activities that address science gaps important to adaptation decisions and policies
   - Build science translation capacity to improve the communication and application of science to meet the needs of decision makers
   Explore approaches to develop an online data and information clearinghouse for adaptation

3. **Address Key Cross-Cutting Issues** – *The breadth of certain climate change impacts creates challenges that cut across the jurisdictions and missions of individual Federal agencies. Addressing these issues will require a collaborative approach along with coordination and partnerships at the local, state, Tribal, and regional levels. The Task Force focused on an initial set of cross-cutting issues and recommends the following actions:*

Improve water resource management *in a changing climate*

- Strengthen data and information systems for understanding climate change impacts on water
- Improve water-use efficiency to reduce climate change impacts
- Develop a national action plan to strengthen climate change adaptation for freshwater resources

Protect human health by addressing climate change in **public health** *activities*

- Enhance the ability of Federal decision makers to incorporate health considerations into adaptation planning
- Build integrated public health surveillance and early warning systems to improve detection of climate change health risks
- Promote resilience of individuals and communities to climate-related health risks

Build resilience to climate change in **communities**

- Ensure relevant Federal regulations, policies, and guidance demonstrate leadership on community adaptation
- Integrate adaptation considerations into Federal programs that affect communities

Facilitate the incorporation of climate change risks into **insurance** *mechanisms*

- Explore a public/private partnership to produce an open-source risk assessment model

Address additional cross-cutting issues

- Develop a strategic action plan focused on strengthening the resilience of coastal, ocean, and Great Lakes communities and ecosystems to climate change
- Develop a strategy for reducing the impacts of climate change on the nation's fish, wildlife, and plant resources and their habitats[1]

4. **Enhance Efforts to Lead and Support International Adaptation**
    – *Climate change poses risks and opportunities that are important to many of the U.S. Government's international development, security, and diplomatic priorities.*
    Climate change adaptation should be a core consideration in the design and implementation of U.S. foreign assistance activities. Agencies should enhance collaboration to support international adaptation objectives.
    - Develop a Government-wide strategy to support multilateral and bilateral adaptation activities and integrate adaptation into relevant U.S. foreign assistance programs
    - Enhance collaboration on adaptation among international development, national security, and technical support agencies
    - Engage global development partners and the private sector to promote knowledge sharing and coordinate investments

5. **Coordinate Capabilities of the Federal Government to Support Adaptation** – *The federal government should improve coordination of its science, services, and assessments to better support stakeholders.*
    - Build and maintain strong partnerships to increase responsiveness of federal government activities to support local, state, and Tribal needs
    - Develop regional climate change adaptation consortia among Federal agencies
    - Establish performance metrics for evaluating Federal adaptation efforts

[1] Pursuant to Congressional direction, development of a national plan to address fish, wildlife, and plant resources is already underway.

PART ONE. INTRODUCTION

The global climate is changing, and the impacts of this change are being felt across the United States and the world. Climate change affects nearly every aspect of society, from our ecosystems and infrastructure, to our public health and our economic and national security. Preparing our nation for the impacts of climate change requires the collective efforts and collaboration of people and institutions across the country, and the collective resources and ideas of partners throughout the world. Many steps are already being taken to improve our understanding of climate change, increase our capacity to anticipate and prepare for adverse impacts, and reduce man-made factors (namely greenhouse gas emissions) that contribute to climate change. However, further efforts and coordination are required – at all levels of government, and among the private sector, academia, and nongovernmental organizations – to ensure that our response to climate change is effective.

Recognizing the urgency of adaptation and the important role of the federal government in reducing the nation's vulnerability to climate change, President Obama signed an Executive Order in October 2009 that required the Interagency Climate Change Adaptation Task Force (Task Force) to assess what the federal government is doing to adapt to climate change and to provide recommendations for additional actions to support a national adaptation strategy. This report presents the Task Force's initial findings and recommendations. In this report, the Task Force has outlined a set of guiding principles, strategic priorities, and near-term actions that are intended to: (1) further focus and strengthen the federal government's efforts on adaptation; and (2) promote greater coordination and collaboration among stakeholders within and outside the Government to advance a national adaptation strategy.

> "… [T]he people of Hāna, Maui are very concerned about the effects of climate change. Not only has our everyday living been affected, but our culture as well. We depend on our freshwater streams and taro patches (loʻi) for sustenance, which allows us to practice our Hawaiian culture. With the increase in drought, our streams and taro patches have dried up, killing the native aquatic species we gather (ʻoʻopu). … Also, with sea level rise, saltwater intrusion will affect our low-land taro patches and will make the survival of the sources of sustenance, our people, and our practices that much more difficult."
>
> – comments from Hāna, Maui at the Hawaii public outreach meeting

This report is not intended to represent a comprehensive national adaptation strategy, in and of itself. The goals and recommended actions it outlines focus on the federal government's role in a national approach, and are intended to foster collective action toward a common adaptation agenda. These are initial steps in what must be a long-term, iterative approach to building a resilient, healthy, and prosperous nation in the face of a changing climate.

PART TWO. THE IMPORTANCE OF ADAPTATION

Climate change is affecting many aspects of our society, our livelihoods, and our environment. Communities across the nation are experiencing climate change impacts, such as changes in average temperatures, more extreme weather events, and rising sea levels.[3] Historically, societies and ecosystems have adjusted or adapted to natural variability in climatic conditions. However, the pace and impacts of climate change are occurring outside the range of past experiences, rendering many of our current□ adaptive mechanisms insufficient. In addition, climate change impacts do not act in isolation; rather, climate-related changes interact with and often magnify the impacts of existing nonclimatic stressors. Decision-makers across the nation will need to take proactive measures to better understand and prepare for current and future changes in climate conditions.

DEFINITIONS FOR KEY TERMS IN THIS DOCUMENT[1]

- **Adaptation**: Adjustment in natural or human systems to a new or changing environment that exploits beneficial opportunities or moderates negative effects.
- **Resilience**: A capability to anticipate, prepare for, respond to, and recover from significant multi-hazard threats with minimum damage to social well- being, the economy, and the environment.
- **Vulnerability**: The degree to which a system is susceptible to, or unable to cope with, adverse effects of climate change, including climate variability and extremes.
- **Mitigation**: An intervention to reduce the causes of changes in climate, such as through reducing emissions of greenhouse gases to the atmosphere.

[1] *Adapting to the Impacts of Climate Change*, America's Climate Choices: Panel on Adapting to the Impacts of Climate Change, National Research Council, (2010).

There is scientific consensus that the Earth's climate is changing due to increased concentrations of greenhouse gases (including carbon dioxide) in the atmosphere.[4,5,6] As a result, increased energy trapped in the atmosphere and the oceans due to these higher concentrations is already leading to impacts, including warmer average water and air temperatures (Figure 1), in the United States and globally.

The Obama Administration is committed to reducing greenhouse gas emissions to minimize the future impacts of climate change. However, the climate impacts we are observing today will continue to increase, at least in the short-term, regardless of the degree to which greenhouse gas emissions are managed. This is driven by factors such as the long-lived nature of certain greenhouse gases in the atmosphere and the absorption of heat by the Earth's oceans. Even if we reduce our emissions, global average temperatures are predicted to rise over the next 100 years (Figure 2).[7] In the long-term, the ability to manage greenhouse gas emissions and moderate or reduce atmospheric concentrations of greenhouse gases will affect the magnitude of the impacts to which we will need to adapt.[8] Therefore, mitigation and adaptation are inextricably linked, and both are required in order to reduce the impacts of climate change.

The scope, severity, and pace of future climate change are difficult to predict with precision; however, observations and long-term trends indicate that the potential impacts of a changing climate on society and the environment will be significant. The 2009 U.S. Global Change Research Program (USGCRP) report, *Global Climate Change Impacts in the United States,* documents climate change impacts to our nation that already have been observed. These impacts include increased average temperatures, more frequent heat waves and high-intensity precipitation events, higher sea levels, and more prolonged droughts, among others.[9] The year-round average air temperature of the U.S. has already risen by more than 2°F over the past 50 years and is projected to increase more in the future.[10] In addition, the intensity of severe precipitation events has increased across the U.S. over the last 50 years (Figure 3), and continued increases in both frequency and intensity of the heaviest downpours are projected in the future. At the same time, the number of dry days is projected to increase, especially in the more arid areas, with the Midwest and the Southwest particularly threatened by drought.[11]

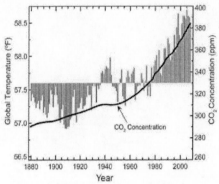

[1] *Global Climate Change Impacts in the United States*, Karl, Thomas R., Melillo, Jerry M., Peterson, Thomas C., (2009).

Figure 1. Global annual average temperature (as measured over both land and oceans) and carbon dioxide concentration from 1880 to present day. Red bars indicate temperatures above and blue bars indicate temperatures below the average temperature for the period 1901-2000. Year-to-year fluctuations in temperature are due to natural processes, such as the effects of El Niños, La Niñas, and the eruption of large volcanoes.[1]

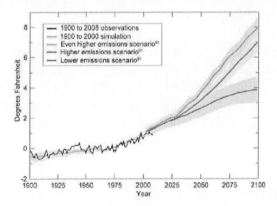

[2] *Ibid.*

Figure 2. Observed and projected changes in the global average temperature under three IPCC emissions scenarios. The lines show the central projections from a set of climate models, and the shaded areas indicate the likely ranges of these projections. A wider range of model types shows outcomes from 2 to 11.5°F. Changes are relative to the 1960-1979 average.[2]

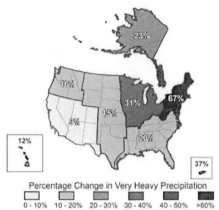

[1] *Global Climate Change Impacts in the United States*, Karl, Thomas R., Melillo, Jerry M., Peterson, Thomas C., (2009).

Figure 3. Percent increases in the amount falling in very heavy precipitation events (defined as the heaviest 1% of all daily events) from 1958 to 2007 for each region.[1]

Climate impacts, both within the United States and across the globe, will not be distributed evenly. For instance, temperature increases in the last ten years have generally been greatest in the northern latitudes (Figure 4). Temperatures in Alaska have increased by approximately twice as much as in the rest of the nation, with significant impacts on sea ice, ecosystems, and coastal communities.[12]

The uneven nature of climate change impacts creates differing levels of vulnerability across countries, communities, and even households, with important implications for adaptive actions. In addition, non-climatic stressors can interact with and exacerbate the impacts of climate stressors. Social and economic factors (e.g., economic status, race, ethnicity, age, gender, and health) can significantly affect people's exposure and sensitivity to climate change, as well as their ability to recover. As with human populations, certain ecosystems (e.g., coral reefs, wetlands, Arctic habitats) are particularly vulnerable to the impacts of climate change. In addition, ecosystems that are degraded or depleted due to non-climatic stressors (e.g., habitat destruction, overharvesting, pollution) have lower resilience to climate change. The effects of climate change on species, habitats, and ecosystems are pervasive and significant across the globe. Impacts of climate change on ecosystem services – the benefits ecosystems provide that humans depend on, such as clean water, oastal protection, flood protection, food production, and recreation – are a major concern.

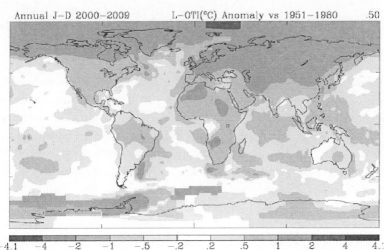

Annual J–D 2000–2009   L–OTI(°C) Anomaly vs 1951–1980   .50

-4.1   -4   -2   -1   -.5   -.2   .2   .5   1   2   4   4.:

[1]*Advancing the Science of Climate Change*, America's Climate Choices: Panel on Advancing the Science of Climate Change, National Research Council, (2010).

Figure 4. Average surface temperature trends (degrees per decade) for Adaptation includes a wide range of the decade 2000-2009 relative to the 1950-1979 average. Warming was more pronounced at high latitudes, especially in the Northern Hemisphere and over land[1]

> *"A hurricane is a threat that you can see in the local news. You can see it coming, marching across the ocean. You can see where it's headed and what to expect when it hits. You can plan for the recovery and for an eventual return to normal. With climate change there's no return to normal."*
> – Honorable Katy Sorenson, Miami-Dade County Commissioner and Chair, Budget, Planning and Sustainability at the Miami public outreach meeting

Adaptation includes a wide range of activities to build resilience and reduce vulnerability to climate change, such as: a farmer growing a different crop variety better suited to warmer or drier conditions; a company relocating key facilities away from coastal areas vulnerable to sea level rise and hurricanes; a community updating its ordinances to protect wetland habitat that provides critical ecosystem services; a city developing early warning systems for severe storms; and a county increasing its water-use efficiency to prepare for more frequent droughts.

PART THREE. THE ROLE OF THE FEDERAL GOVERNMENT IN ADAPTING TO CLIMATE CHANGE

Multiple stakeholders, including governmental, non-governmental, and private organizations, must work together across different scales and sectors to successfully adapt to climate change. The federal government has an important and unique role in this collective process. In particular, Federal leadership, guidance, and support are important to help design and implement actions based on the best available information, science, and technology. Just as importantly, the federal government must work in partnership with communities, Tribes, and states – many of which are already beginning to implement adaptation measures – because climate impacts span political boundaries. To effectively adapt to climate change, stakeholders in affected regions should coordinate their responses to climate impacts on shared infrastructure and resources.

The federal government should promote best practices for adaptation to build greater public awareness and understanding of the importance of adaptation, and maintain critical dialogue and partnerships with stakeholders and decision makers. The federal government must enhance its ability to provide public and private actors with accessible and localized climate risk, impact, and vulnerability information to support their decision making. Furthermore, the federal government should continue to work with the international community to increase our scientific understanding of climate change and improve global coordination in responding to climate impacts.

The federal government also has an important stake in adaptation because climate change directly affects Federal services, operations, and programs across the country. Virtually every aspect of the federal government will be impacted by climate change in some way. The Government must exercise leadership in addressing climate impacts on Federal infrastructure interests and on the natural, cultural, and historic resources that it has statutory responsibilities to protect. Climate change will also affect our national security. Adaptation requires careful planning to incorporate appropriate strategies in agency missions and operations to ensure that Federal resources are invested wisely and that agency services and operations remain effective. The federal government must coordinate its adaptation strategies with local, state, and Tribal partners, as the majority of effective adaptation strategies are implemented at the local to regional scale.

Agencies should work individually, collaboratively, and with the Task Force to ensure that resources are allocated to maximize their impact and avoid unnecessary duplication. In the current fiscal climate, agencies should implement the recommendations in this report with the understanding that activities will be funded within current overall budget amounts and guidance.

PART FOUR. THE INTERAGENCY CLIMATE CHANGE ADAPTATION TASK FORCE

The Interagency Climate Change Adaptation Task Force (Task Force) began meeting in Spring 2009. The Task Force is co-chaired by the Council on Environmental Quality (CEQ), the National Oceanic and Atmospheric Administration (NOAA), and the Office of Science and Technology Policy (OSTP). The Executive Order signed by the President in October 2009 required the Task Force to deliver a report through the Chair of CEQ to the President within one year to outline progress on agency actions in support of a national strategy and recommendations for additional actions.

The Task Force, composed of over 20 Federal agencies and Executive branch offices, formed workgroups to consider the federal government's capabilities to respond to climate change impacts on various critical sectors, institutions, and agency mission responsibilities. Over 300 Federal employees participated in the Task Force and its workgroups over the past year (Appendices A and B).

The Task Force considered many adaptation initiatives, challenges, and opportunities as it developed this report. Ongoing and emerging Federal agency climate change initiatives, including the USGCRP 2009 report, *Global Climate Change Impacts in the United States,* provided a basis for the work of the Task Force. In addition, the Task Force and its workgroups conducted over 35 public outreach meetings, listening sessions, and other public engagement events over the last year to gain greater perspective on how climate change is affecting our nation and what steps the federal government can take to foster a more coordinated and effective national response. Stakeholders at these events conveyed input and ideas that were integral to the Task Force's work and helped shape the vision, guiding principles, and recommendations articulated in this report. Maintaining a sustained and meaningful dialogue with stakeholders will continue to be an essential element of the federal government's approach to adaptation.

> *"We work closely with communities to help governments, businesses and residents to understand their disaster risk and what they can do to prevent, prepare for, and be more resilient to natural disasters....Our concern with the increase and frequency of extreme weather events, and our increase in emergency response, is the most "at risk" individuals. How can we do more to prepare our individuals, especially the most vulnerable, for the unexpected?"*
>
> — Lisa Hunter, American Red Cross at the Chicago public outreach meeting

PART FIVE. STRATEGIC VISION AND GUIDING PRINCIPLES FOR ADAPTATION POLICY AND ACTIONS

The work of the Task Force has been guided by a strategic vision of a resilient, healthy, and prosperous nation in the face of a changing climate. The United States must adapt to climate change in order to safeguard people, places, and natural resources both domestically and abroad. Our nation is committed to reducing greenhouse gas emissions to limit the magnitude of future climate change, but impacts will continue to occur. We must respond to those impacts that are already happening and prepare for future ones. Climate change adaptation requires not only innovative technology and ideas, but also meaningful changes to policies, behavior, and institutions. Adaptation provides an opportunity to revisit the way that business is conducted and to improve existing policies and practices, including those that increase vulnerability, in order to ensure a more sustainable future.

Guiding Principles

To support these efforts, the Task Force has identified a set of guiding principles that should be considered in the design and implementation of adaptation strategies.

- **Adopt integrated approaches**. Climate change preparation and response should be integrated into core policies, planning, practices, and programs whenever possible.

- **Prioritize the most vulnerable.** Adaptation plans should prioritize helping people, places, and infrastructure that are most vulnerable to climate impacts. They should also be designed and implemented with meaningful involvement from all parts of society. Issues of inequality and environmental justice associated with climate change impacts and adaptation should be addressed.

- **Use best-available science.** Adaptation should be grounded in best-available scientific understanding of climate change risks, impacts, and vulnerabilities. Adaptive actions should not be delayed to wait for a complete understanding of climate change impacts, as there will always be some uncertainty. Plans and actions should be adjusted as our understanding of climate impacts increases.

- **Build strong partnerships.** Adaptation requires coordination across multiple sectors, geographical scales, and levels of government and should build on the existing efforts and knowledge of a wide range of stakeholders. Because impacts, vulnerability, and needs vary by region and locale, adaptation will be most effective when driven by local or regional risks and needs.

- **Apply risk-management methods and tools.** A risk management approach can be an effective way to assess and respond to climate change because the timing, likelihood, and nature of specific climate risks are difficult to predict. Risk management approaches are already used in many critical decisions today (e.g., for fire, flood, disease outbreaks), and can aid in understanding the potential consequences of inaction as well as options for risk reduction.

- **Apply ecosystem-based approaches.** Ecosystems provide valuable services that help to build resilience and reduce the vulnerability of people and their livelihoods to climate change impacts. Integrating the protection of biodiversity and ecosystem services into adaptation strategies will increase resilience of human and natural systems to climate and non-climate risks, providing benefits to society and the environment.

- **Maximize mutual benefits.** Adaptation should, where possible, use strategies that complement or directly support other related climate or environmental initiatives, such as efforts to improve disaster preparedness, promote sustainable resource management, and reduce greenhouse gas emissions including the development of cost-effective technologies.

Observation systems help us understand changes in the climate so that decisions can be based on the best-available science.

- **Continuously evaluate performance**. Adaptation plans should include measurable goals and performance metrics to continuously assess whether adaptive actions are achieving desired outcomes. In some cases, the measurements will be qualitative until more information is gathered to evaluate outcomes quantitatively. Flexibility is a critical to building a robust and resilient process that can accommodate uncertainty and change.

These principles and concepts are not new. They are being applied in cities around the world that are working to protect health and infrastructure; in states working collaboratively at regional levels to improve management and sustainability of land, water, and energy resources; through the concerns of citizens who live in vulnerable locations; and through the experiences of Federal agencies that are considering how climate change challenges their existing missions, operations, and programs.

PART SIX. CURRENT FEDERAL GOVERNMENT EFFORTS IN SUPPORT OF ADAPTATION

Substantial activities are already underway across the federal government to build adaptive capacity and increase resilience to climate change. These activities include efforts to improve understanding of climate science and impacts, to incorporate climate change considerations into policies and practices, and to strengthen technical support and capacity for adaptation decision making. Some efforts are large collaborative undertakings involving Federal and non-Federal partners while others are smaller and at the program-level. Examples of Federal agencies' current and proposed efforts to support adaptation include:

Interagency Activities

- **USGCRP** has invested significant resources in understanding and modeling the physical science of climate and has also funded research on the implications of climate change for natural systems and human health and welfare. These include observing systems in the oceans, on land, and in the atmosphere; research on climate impacts and vulnerability; and science in support of decision making. USGCRP is currently in the process of establishing a new Adaptation Strategic Program Element to provide accessible information to support adaptation decisions at all scales.

- The **National Climate Assessment** (NCA), which is required every four years under the Global Change Research Act of 1990 and conducted under the USGCRP, will identify science needs for understanding current and future climate impacts and regional or sector-related vulnerability to those impacts, supporting adaptation and mitigation decisions, and informing effective translation of science into services and applications.

> *"Climate change is one of the greatest public health challenges of this century...We have to help raise public awareness and understanding of climate change impacts on health, the need to prepare for these changes, and the need to take strong and urgent actions to reduce emissions in order to avoid the most catastrophic impacts of climate change. And that will only happen if we work closely with local agencies and community based organizations to educate, empower and engage communities in actions to mitigate and adapt to climate change."*
>
> – Dr. Linda Rudolph, Deputy Director of the centers for chronic disease and health promotion, State of California at the Portland public outreach meeting

Agency Activities

- **National Oceanic and Atmospheric Administration's (NOAA)** proposed Climate Service will seek to combine the agency's climate science and technical capabilities with new and existing service development, delivery, and communication capabilities to create an organization that advances scientific understanding, engages users collaboratively, and delivers services.
- The **Department of the Interior (DOI)** is developing a network of eight regional Climate Science Centers and 22 Landscape Conservation Cooperatives to inform science-based adaptation and mitigation strategies and adaptive management techniques in partnership with resource managers. In cooperation with other Federal and state agencies, this network will help to connect natural and cultural resource managers to relevant science support, and work with local partners to provide tailored information for regional adaptation decisions.
- The **Department of Agriculture (USDA)** has integrated climate change objectives into its strategic plans and is expanding its focus on climate-related research and delivery capacity across its agencies to provide climate services to rural and agricultural stakeholders through existing programs, including the Cooperative Extension Service, the Natural Resources Conservation Districts, and the USDA Forest Service's Climate Change Resource Center.
- The **Department of Transportation (DOT)** is analyzing the vulnerabilities of critical transportation infrastructure in the Gulf of Mexico region, and developing risk management tools that can be applied in the Gulf and elsewhere.
- The **Department of Energy (DOE)** is developing energy technologies that will significantly contribute to climate change adaptation, including programs focused on reducing the energy and water intensity of electricity generation and use, and transportation fuels production. DOE is also developing information and tools that will help local and regional planners anticipate climate change effects and adaptation needs.
- The **Environmental Protection Agency (EPA)** is supporting local decision makers through a variety of programs and online tools, including the Climate Ready Estuaries program and the Climate

Ready Water Utilities Working Group. EPA has also taken the lead on a number of regional climate adaptation projects.

- The **Department of Housing and Urban Development's (HUD)** Office of Policy Development and Research is helping to develop a toolkit of HUD initiatives that will provide new resources to communities to address the challenges resulting from climate change and growth patterns at the local level.

- The **National Aeronautics and Space Administration (NASA)** has created an integrated effort between its Earth Science Division and Environmental Management Division to look at the long-term effects of climate change for its Centers, many of which are in climate-sensitive areas, and to enable more informed future planning for its Centers and resource management.

- The **Department of the Navy** established Task Force Climate Change which has developed and begun to implement two roadmaps for climate change adaptation in the Arctic and across the globe. Activities include conducting joint and combined exercises in the Arctic, initiating education on climate change science and security, and incorporating adaptation in Navy strategic objectives and plans.

- The **Department of State** is contributing to adaptation through the U.N. Framework Convention on Climate Change (UNFCCC) and related funding mechanisms, and is leading international efforts to foster more effective coordination among institutions engaged in adaptation.

- The **U.S. Agency for International Development (USAID)** has prepared a guidance document on integrating adaptation into foreign assistance programs, sponsored the development of the Famine Early Warning Systems Network, and developed or contributed to several other analytical tools, databases, and guidance materials on international adaptation.

- The **Department of the Treasury** oversees U.S. contributions to several multilateral investment funds that help developing countries improve their adaptive capacity, such as the UNFCCC Special Climate Change Fund and the World Bank's Pilot Program for Climate Resilience.

- The **Office of Science and Technology Policy (OSTP)** is helping Federal agencies to develop a coherent national architecture for these and other Federal climate assessments and services.

PART SEVEN. FEDERAL POLICY GOALS TO ADVANCE NATIONAL ADAPTATION

The Task Force recommends that the federal government focus on a set of five overarching policy goals that are consistent with the strategic vision and guiding principles described above and build upon current efforts. These policy goals are intended to reinforce existing adaptation efforts, harness a range of capabilities and resources across the federal government, and build strong partnerships with local, state, regional, Tribal, and international stakeholders to achieve a common mission of developing and maintaining a resilient, healthy, and prosperous society in the face of a changing climate.

1. *Encourage and mainstream adaptation planning across the federal government*
2. *Improve integration of science into decision making*
3. *Address key cross-cutting issues*
4. *Enhance efforts to lead and support international adaptation*
5. *Coordinate capabilities of the federal government to support adaptation*

Each goal includes a set of supporting recommendations for near-term action. The Task Force should work over the next year to monitor and support implementation of the recommendations presented below.

Goal 1: Encourage and Mainstream Adaptation Planning across the Federal Government

Climate change will challenge the mission, operations, and programs of nearly every Federal agency. Ensuring the capacity of federal government agencies to execute their missions, domestically and internationally, and maintain essential services in the face of climate change will be a critical factor in successful adaptation as a nation. Agencies should consider how climate change affects them using a flexible, forward-thinking approach that moves away from using past conditions as indicators of the future. This approach should include a commitment to ongoing evaluation and revision of management activities and decisions through adaptive management. Implementing this recommendation requires agencies to identify and address climate vulnerabilities and opportunities and build resilience to climate change. There is no single planning approach appropriate for all agencies; however, using a consistent, but flexible, framework will facilitate coordination across agencies and allow them to leverage common tools and methods.

Recommended Action: Implement adaptation planning within Federal agencies

Individual Federal agencies should establish and implement coordinated climate adaptation action plans that address the unique and interdisciplinary challenges posed by climate change to their missions, operations, and programs. In their adaptation action plans, agencies should identify measures to incorporate climate change-related considerations into existing agency planning processes, including the development of measurable goals and performance metrics to guide adaptation efforts and assess whether efforts are achieving desired outcomes.

This will help to streamline and enhance adaptation efforts currently underway within agencies as well as improve information sharing among agencies, accelerating implementation and learning. Agency adaptation planning will also foster greater attention to and action on critical issues at local, state, Tribal, and regional levels.

> *"We can all relate to the very tangible impacts of a changing climate (for example – streets flooded during extreme rain storms, extended seasons for garden vegetables). Because we are talking about real, contemporary experiences when we talk about adaptation – we have a chance to talk about facts and about real, achievable actions. And a chance to learn about science and problem-solving."*
> – Anonymous at the Chicago public outreach meeting

The Executive Office of the President should support the implementation of agency adaptation planning. Implementation should follow a similar planning process to that used for sustainability planning under Executive Order 13514 on Federal Leadership in Environmental, Energy, and Economic Performance, in which the CEQ Office of the Federal Environmental Executive (OFEE) works in concert with the Office of Management and Budget (OMB). The CEQ Chair will issue implementing instructions to agencies within 120 days of this report. The Agency Adaptation Workgroup formed under the Task Force should be engaged and support OFEE in this process.

As agency planning moves forward, there is also an opportunity to develop common tools to improve the effectiveness and efficiency of implementing climate change adaptation across the federal government.

Agencies should work with OFEE and OMB to identify and coordinate the development of common and shared effective tools for science translation, economic and decision analysis, and evaluation of agency adaptation efforts.

Recommended Action: Employ a flexible framework for agency adaptation planning

Federal agency adaptation planning should be based on a six-step flexible planning framework to enable a process that is both consistent and tailored to the specific planning needs of each agency. The flexible framework (Figure 5) highlights the need to build agency skills and capacity; develop an adaptation mandate with success measures; assess and understand the substantial risks, vulnerabilities, and opportunities posed by climate change; develop, prioritize, and implement adaptation actions; and evaluate the results and lessons learned from the process to improve future adaptation.

The flexible framework is not meant to provide a detailed set of options for implementing actions at the local or project level, but rather to enable agencies to identify key vulnerabilities across their programs, set priorities, and begin to take action. The core elements of the flexible framework are as follows:

- *Set mandate.* Effective adaptation planning and implementation requires a mandate with clear objectives and metrics. This step of the flexible framework asks, "What are our goals?" and "What is success?" These questions must be answered in the context of each agency's missions and operations. Agencies should establish leadership-level directives that are tailored to agency missions.
- *Understand how climate is changing.* At this step, agencies should answer the following types of questions using the best-available science: "What aspects of the climate are changing and over what timescale? What uncertainties are associated with projected impacts of climate change in the context of other stresses, and how can we build this uncertainty into our adaptation efforts?" This may also require consideration of low-probability but high-impact scenarios.

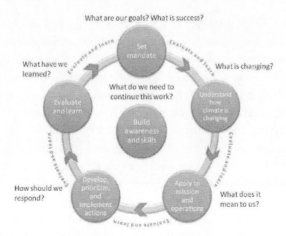

Figure 5. Six step approach to climate change adaptation planning.

- *Apply to mission and operations.* Agencies should ask at this step "What do these changes mean to us?" Agencies' answers to this question specifically consider the risks, vulnerabilities and opportunities posed by climate change to agency missions and operations. Agencies can build on their experience and skill in decision making in the face of uncertainty as they rely on the best-available science to consider potential impacts on their mission and operations in the context of existing stressors.
- *Develop, prioritize, and implement actions.* Agency decision makers must face the question of "How should we respond?" To answer this question, agencies must consider a comprehensive set of potential climate adaptation measures – including infrastructural, technological, behavioral, and risk management measures. Criteria for selecting priority adaptation activities and projects will vary from agency to agency, and it is difficult to provide a comprehensive list that will be applicable and realistic for each Federal agency.
- *Evaluate and learn.* Successful climate adaptation requires ongoing monitoring and evaluation of adaptation planning efforts to continually assess the effectiveness of actions and adjust as necessary. Because of the uncertainties inherent in projecting future climate conditions, impacts, and responses, adaptation cannot be simply a policy or action that requires a one-time change. All adaptation plans must allow for a "feedback" mechanism, whereby new knowledge and information, lessons learned (including costs of implementation),

and modified priorities can be accounted for and incorporated into the ongoing adaptation process. Performance metrics should be developed and used to determine whether desired outcomes are being achieved.

- *Build awareness and skills.* Building awareness and skills is central to ensuring the sustainability of adaptation planning, implementation, and evaluation. This element builds agency capacity for ongoing monitoring, assessment, and management of climate effects, responses, and adaptation. Building awareness and skills will require education and training, role models, enabling structures, and a compelling narrative or mandate.

Several pilot tests of the flexible framework are currently underway – from agency-wide to the individual project level. The Department of Homeland Security (DHS) is conducting a high-level, agency-wide pilot with its agency components. DOT is conducting a pilot through the Federal Highway Administration (FHWA) that will be tested at the state or Metropolitan Planning Organization level. EPA is conducting a community-level pilot in Iowa, involving other Federal, state, and local agencies. The U.S Army Corps of Engineers (USACE) is performing several project-level pilots in representative business areas at different phases of the project lifecycle and range of scales.[13]

Recommended Action: Use a phased and coordinated approach to implement agency adaptation

Most Federal agencies will take a phased approach to implementing adaptation planning based on the risks and capacity unique to each agency. Agencies may have to first consider the climate change adaptation planning process at a conceptual level in order to build awareness and to make the case internally for prioritizing these issues before investing in the development of a strategic plan. During an initial phase, agencies could be asked to produce a high-level plan, identify priority areas, set goals for adaptation efforts, and identify their own performance metrics moving forward.

This phased approach does not mean that agencies should wait to take advantage of relevant opportunities. Targeted, near-term adaptive actions should be advanced even as broader, long-term planning efforts are undertaken. For example, in metropolitan areas, HUD can assess building codes and other guidelines for implementation of housing adaptation strategies that address low- and moderate-income housing among other changing housing needs. DOT can develop methods to include climate risk analysis in transportation investment policies, promote vulnerability assessments, and assess and update, as needed, transportation design standards. DOE can work with utilities and other electricity generators to assess water requirements and implications for local water supplies, and provide more precise answers to the questions that decision makers must resolve when dealing with the intertwined issues of climate, water, and energy. Similarly, programs like the National Flood Insurance Program (NFIP) in the Federal Emergency Management Agency (FEMA) can explore a range of approaches to encourage people, communities, and businesses to shift away from high-risk coastal areas and account for future risk in the administration of the Program.

> "*[The federal government should] use the precautionary principle to encourage cities to plan for greater uncertainty and variability when building green and grey infrastructure by asking [Request For Proposal] respondents to describe how their planned projects adapt to climate change.*"
> — Joyce Coffee, City of Chicago at the Chicago public outreach meeting

The adaptation planning process of individual agencies should catalyze and support enhanced coordination across Federal agencies. As agencies identify priority areas and set their goals for climate change adaptation, they should consult with other agencies that share equities and common concerns, particularly in areas that are cross-cutting. Agency plans should, as appropriate, describe how other agencies were consulted, articulate specific plans for collaboration, and identify areas in which targeting of a different part of the issue by another agency represents the most effective approach to a given problem. Federal agencies' regional offices should also be engaged as they often have the most direct involvement at the intersection of climate impacts and Federal, local, state, Tribal, and regional actors. An agency's regional offices should coordinate with the regional offices of other Federal agencies in the context of their agency adaptation planning process (see the Goal 5 recommended action on regional adaptation consortia).

Goal 2: Improve Integration of Science into Decision Making

Integrated, interdisciplinary science is critical for understanding and envisioning a range of potential climate impacts, informing adaptive actions, and evaluating the effectiveness of response options. Federal agencies should provide tools to enable the science, as well as the translation and communication of that science, to meet the needs of information users (e.g., decision makers, planners, resource managers, general public) as they work to reduce the impacts of climate change to infrastructure, ecosystems, and human health and welfare. Using science translation and tools to effectively integrate science into the decision making process will help individuals and institutions confront uncertainties about future outcomes with improved information about risks and opportunities in order to make informed decisions.

Recommended Action: Create a "roadmap" of existing Federal science efforts that inform and support adaptation

Many programs across the federal government produce science that informs and supports climate change adaptation decision making. Many of these efforts occur through the agencies of the USGCRP, while others have emerged in resource management or community development programs through agencies that have not historically focused on climate change. Currently, most of these activities are occurring independently of one another, leading to gaps and redundancies. These efforts would benefit from enhanced coordination on science at the Federal level, through agencies working together more closely to leverage existing capabilities. Coordination would help Federally sponsored science identify, understand, and meet the needs of decision makers implementing adaptation strategies on the ground.

The new Adaptation Science and Research Element within the USGCRP should develop a "roadmap" that identifies existing adaptation science and service capabilities and gaps across Federally-sponsored programs. The roadmap will help to identify existing and emerging connections across Federal agencies that share responsibilities, and between Federal agencies and their local, state, Tribal, or international partners. This activity will need to be coordinated across all Federal agencies, not just those currently under the USGCRP, with particular attention on identifying relevant non-Federal partnerships that agencies consider critical to their adaptation work. The "roadmap" should also build upon the efforts of the Task Force's Adaptation

Science Workgroup over the past year to identify key issues related to science that supports adaptation decisions. In addition, the "roadmap" should include all relevant science fields required for adaptation efforts, including disciplines beyond the traditional physical "climate science" such as social and behavioral sciences and ecology, as well as interdisciplinary efforts.

Recommended Action: Prioritize activities that address science gaps important to adaptation decisions and policies

The federal government should prioritize scientific activities that address critical gaps in understanding to better inform and support adaptation decisions. USGCRP should consider options for identifying and expanding opportunities to address these gaps through interagency coordination and its strategic planning process. Key actions to address science gaps identified include:

- Develop scenarios of a range of climate change outcomes at spatial and temporal scales necessary to inform impact assessment and adaptive action.
- Create user-friendly methods for assessing climate impacts, vulnerability, and risk, including models and tools to assess the environmental, social, and economic outcomes of alternative adaptation actions.
- Provide guidance on the use and suitability of downscaled global climate model outputs.
- Conduct frequent updates of regional characterizations and assessments of climate, including climate-driven variables (e.g., stream flow, flood, and drought).
- Expand research on relevant social and behavioral sciences to improve understanding of human responses to change.
- Identify the social and ecological tipping points and thresholds (beyond which change is sudden and potentially irreversible) to help guide decisions regarding intervention and planning.
- Develop methods and processes for identifying, defining, and managing for extremes, including low-probability, high-impact events.
- Analyze climate change impacts in the context of multiple stressors and interacting systems (e.g., interactions of climate and air quality on human health in metropolitan areas).

> *"One thing we know for sure is we're not going to be able to move forward doing this alone. That's the reason the four counties in South Florida have come together [and] agreed to work on modeling in the same way, with the same timelines."*
> – Honorable Kristin Jacobs, Broward County Commissioner and Chair, Climate Change Task Force at the Miami public outreach meeting

Recommended Action: Build science translation capacity to improve the communication and application of science to meet the needs of decision makers

The federal government should enhance its capacity to translate information between scientists and decision makers. Effective science translation will help to ensure that decision makers have the information they need to make decisions on adaptive measures. For example, a municipality would need access to and translation of sea level rise scenarios in order to make an informed decision regarding a long-term investment in sewage treatment infrastructure to prepare for future climate change. Online infrastructure can also support these efforts by improving the accessibility of information and share lessons learned both to and from end users.

Science translation is facilitated by experts who help to connect the information needs of decision makers to best-available science. Rather than continuing the science-led approach to providing climate information, the federal government should translate science in a collaborative and multi-directional way. The federal government should consider decision makers needs when prioritizing scientific research for science to be useful to adaptation planning.

To effectively integrate and implement adaptation responses, the federal government should recruit, develop, and retain technically capable staff that have the proper expertise to understand decision maker needs, and to communicate effectively climate change impacts.

Federal agencies should evaluate their existing ability to deliver and translate science for users and invest in building this capability. There are excellent examples of successful science-to-user continuums from which to learn (e.g., NOAA Coastal Services Center, National Integrated Drought Information System, Federal Climate Change and Water Working Group, Joint Fire Science Program, U.S. Geological Survey (USGS)/U.S. Fish and Wildlife Service (USFWS) wildlife impact collaborations). The USDA Cooperative Extension and NOAA Sea Grant Extension currently provide extension agents of all specializations with training in understanding and communicating climate change information to support adaptation; these efforts should be expanded. Translation can provide extremely useful connections between practical management challenges and the best-available science.

Recommended Action: Explore approaches to develop an online data and information clearinghouse for adaptation

Agencies within the Task Force are in the early stages of an effort to adapt the NOAA Climate Services Portal prototype, currently hosted at Climate.gov, into an operational interagency online portal that brings together climate science and services information from across the federal government. Climate.gov is an easily identifiable, authoritative online source of climate information where the public can access data, tools, and informational resources to help them understand climate science as well as options for adaptation and mitigation.

These agencies should also work together with the NCA to identify the necessary components of an online data and information clearinghouse for adaptation, including next steps for development and implementation, and a mechanism for the ongoing maintenance and updating of this resource. They should evaluate the appropriate roles for the federal government in identifying, compiling, and enhancing data collection efforts across the Government on key climate impact indicators, as well as catalyzing, developing, and supporting these clearinghouse components over the long-term. In addition, potential roles for private and public partners should be explored. Components could include: scientific information, transferable decision-support tools, best practices, relevant contacts from adaptation activities across the nation, and an active support mechanism to facilitate dialogue among users.

Goal 3: Address Key Cross-Cutting Issues

Given the breadth of climate change impacts and corresponding adaptation measures, certain key climate-related issues will require a collaborative approach from the federal government, such as water resource management, public health activities, community resilience, and insurance risk assessment. Such adaptation issues cut across the jurisdictions and missions of individual Federal agencies and will require extensive coordination and partnerships at the local, state, Tribal, regional, and international levels. For these cross-cutting adaptation issues, a collaborative approach is necessary to ensure that adaptation actions are timely, do not duplicate the work of other Government agencies, fill critical gaps, and maximize the returns on the federal government's investments in adaptation.

The Task Force began addressing crosscutting issues through an initial set of issue-focused workgroups: water resource management, public health, resilient communities[14] and the role of insurance. While these issues are all critically important, they were selected based on existing interest and capacity to serve as venues for interagency dialogue. Additional cross-cutting issues will need to be addressed in a comprehensive national approach to adaptation. Moving forward, the Task Force will work to identify, prioritize, and address these issues. The recommended actions described below reflect the work of the issue-focused workgroups on the topics addressed in the initial year of the Task Force's activities.

Recommended Action: Improve water resource management in a changing climate

A changing climate is expected to have major consequences for the nation's water resources. On average, water temperatures are predicted to increase. Rainfall amounts will decline in some areas and increase in other areas.[15,16] The proportion of precipitation that falls as snow will decrease; and rainfall and storm events will become more intense. In the case of coastal and ocean waters, the impacts of climate change include rising sea levels, more saline estuarine waters, and more acidic ocean waters.[17,18] These impacts are already posing significant challenges for water resources management in several major areas: assuring adequate water supply (e.g. for drinking water, agriculture, irrigation, energy, etc.); protecting human life, health, and property; and protecting the quality of freshwater resources.

Water resource managers will need to cope with prolonged drought in some areas due to climate change.

The Task Force's Water Resource Workgroup has identified the following actions to improve water resource management in a changing climate:

> *"We farm a ground that my grandfathers had farmed. This is not just a job or even a career – this is a legacy, a life.... And just one year could wipe all of that out. So we take these [climate change adaptation] policies and these issues very seriously."*
> – Wayne Hurst, Vice President, National Wheat Growers Association
> at the Denver public outreach meeting

Strengthen data and information systems for understanding climate change impacts on water

DOI is leading an interagency effort to build a national system that will describe the changing availability, quality, location, and uses of water resources. This information system should be organized by watershed and made available to water managers and the public.

The effort should include evaluation of these water data as needed to provide water resource managers and engineers engaged in infrastructure planning, water management decisions, ecosystem protection, and flood hazard mitigation with the interpretative "hydrostatistics" that are needed to make good decisions as hydrological conditions change over time. Examples of these statistics include precipitation frequency estimates, probable maximum precipitation estimates, and streamflow estimates for multiple time scales.

Actions needed to strengthen data and information systems for water in response to a changing climate will be described in more detail in a Report to Congress in March 2011, as required under Section 9506 of the Omnibus Public Lands Act.

Improve water-use efficiency to reduce climate change impacts

Increasing water-use efficiency helps to extend the availability of current supplies, save energy, reduce the cost of water system operations, maintenance, and replacement, protect the environment, and prepare for increased climate-driven variability in the hydrologic cycle. Key steps to improve water-use efficiency may include:

- Establishing nationally consistent metrics of water-use efficiency for municipal water systems, energy producers, irrigation suppliers, and other users of water, and defining a mechanism to make these data transparent and readily available to decision makers and the public;

- Revising existing Federal guidelines related to environmental assessments required under both the National Environmental Policy Act and the "Principles and Standards" that guide Federal water resource projects to more clearly address opportunities for water-use efficiency and water reuse;

- Identifying and sharing examples of excellence in improving water-use efficiency, and developing and deploying innovative and cost-effective water-efficient technologies in key water use sectors (e.g., drinking water, agriculture, irrigation, energy) and regions of the country as a means to facilitate wider adoption of practices.

Develop a national action plan to strengthen climate change adaptation for freshwater resources

A national action plan should be developed to ensure an effective, well-coordinated, and sustained approach to adapting the nation's freshwater resources to a changing climate. The existing Task Force Water Resources Workgroup should lead the development of this adaptation plan. The Workgroup should engage a diverse range of stakeholders in this effort through the existing DOI *Advisory Committee on Water Information* and work with regional coordination partnerships wherever available. The Workgroup should also coordinate with existing interagency organizations, such as the National Science and Technology Council's *Subcommittee on Water Availability and Quality* and the *Climate Change and Water Working Group*, on issues related to water science and research. In addition to developing the action plan for freshwater resources, the Workgroup should oversee related activities including the development of the Report to Congress on water resources data and information needs related to climate change and expanded efforts to improve water use efficiency described above.

The freshwater action plan should be coordinated with the National Ocean Council's efforts for coastal and ocean water resources as described in the *Final Recommendations of the Interagency Ocean Policy Task Force*, where appropriate.

Recommended Action: Protect human health by addressing climate change in public health activities

Climate change has emerged as an important public health challenge, both in the United States and globally. The potential health effects of climate change include heat-related illness and death; injuries, toxic exposures, mental health and stress disorders, and other impacts from severe weather events; cardiovascular and respiratory illnesses from worsening air pollution and allergen exposure; and increased rates of infectious diseases. These effects may be particularly severe for low-income and minority populations, native peoples, children, the elderly, and the physically infirm, among others. Furthermore, because many health problems cross international borders, global health cannot be separated from U.S. interests. Adaptive actions must be undertaken to anticipate these changes and avoid or reduce potential harmful health impacts. Since many of the health impacts of climate change in the United States can be addressed by strengthening existing public health systems, health is a critical area where the federal government can implement "no regrets" policies and actions. Specific actions that the federal government can take to manage the public health implications of climate change include the following:

Enhance the ability of Federal decision makers to incorporate health considerations into adaptation planning

The federal government recognizes that decision makers in all fields should consider the health effects of climate adaptation options in their planning efforts. To achieve the goal of encouraging health analysis as part of adaptation planning, science must be integrated into all levels of decision making. That integration requires the ability to identify and analyze health impacts, which in turn requires methods and standards for conducting the analyses and for determining whether such analyses are sufficient. OSTP, working with the USGCRP, the Department of Health and Human Services (HHS), and others should convene an interagency effort to review current methodologies and standards, their uncertainties and limitations, and to assist decision makers by developing and providing tools and guidance for determining when and how to consider health impacts.

> "[The federal government] can empower local health departments by strengthening existing and building new capacity in the areas of public health surveillance, GIS mapping, and conducting vulnerability assessments..."
>
> – Kari Lyons-Eubanks, Policy Analyst, Multnomah County Environmental Health Services, State of Oregon at the Portland public outreach meeting

Build integrated public health surveillance and early warning systems to improve detection of climate change health risks

A critical component of assessing health vulnerabilities to climate change is the ability to collect and analyze data related to health outcomes, underlying vulnerabilities, adaptive capacity, and measures of resilience. Integrating human health data with animal and ecosystem health data is vital to understanding and addressing the complexities of many vector-borne, water-borne, food-borne, and other diseases. Integrating health data with demographic, geographic, and climatic data is also critical for gaining full understanding of underlying vulnerabilities. Currently, incompatibility of datasets in these different disciplines presents a significant barrier to data integration.

> *"Sixty percent of the sewer system in Broward County is gravity fed. When the sea level rises and sewage is no longer running downhill, we'll have a lot more believers [calling on us] to do something."*
> – Honorable Kristin Jacobs, Broward County Commissioner and Chair, Climate Change Task Force at the Miami public outreach meeting

Agencies (including HHS, NOAA, USDA, NASA, DOI) that collect and maintain these datasets should prioritize developing methods to better integrate their datasets to facilitate health analyses. This data integration would allow for development of early warning systems that could improve our ability to detect current and emerging health risks.

The federal government can provide information and tools to help communities prepare for and respond to climate change impacts, like flooding.

Promote resilience of individuals and communities to climate-related health risks

Individual resilience to climate change health impacts may be improved by promoting healthier behaviors, such as increasing physical activity and improving nutrition to respond appropriately to extreme heat and weather events and reducing risks of climate sensitive chronic diseases. Community-level resilience could be enhanced through prioritizing programs to reduce health disparities, particularly among vulnerable subpopulations; strengthening emergency preparedness, response, and recovery functions at the local, state, and Tribal levels; promoting social support systems within communities; and improving infrastructure (e.g., hospitals and other health delivery facilities, drinking water, sewage, transportation, and energy systems). Since this public health-related infrastructure is a long-term investment, ensuring that it is resilient to climate change will best protect health in the decades to come.

Recommended Action: Build resilience to climate change in communities

Adaptation planning for communities and their underlying infrastructure is crucial. Federal interest and investment in communities include transportation, housing, water and water infrastructure, health, public safety, emergency preparedness and response, and energy. Investments in community infrastructure are generally long-term, difficult to reverse, and resource-intensive, emphasizing the importance of "getting it right the first time."

> *"We are working hard to promote "green" (ecosystem-based) adaptation – actions that have the goal of making both people and wild species more resilient to climate change by reducing stressors on, and restoring, natural systems. In many cases, we are working with new collaborative partners, like stormwater engineers, or corporations with goals to reduce their water footprint. Our work could greatly benefit from programs that provide incentives or preferences for adaptation actions that incorporate investments in natural systems, and for partnerships that actively involve conservation/restoration practitioners."*
> – Kim Hall, The Nature Conservancy Great Lakes Project at the Chicago public outreach meeting

Climate change impacts that will most affect communities – whether urban, suburban, or rural – include extreme heat, poor air quality, increased flooding, higher storm surges, and sea level rise. Reducing vulnerability and enhancing resilience of community infrastructure present challenges that require coordination among public and private interests, local to national jurisdictions, and within localities (e.g., zoning, building codes, and emergency management). Additionally, community decision makers will need to take special care to protect socially and culturally vulnerable populations who are particularly at risk from climate change impacts, including Tribes, low-income and minority populations, children, the elderly, and the physically infirm.

Specific measures the federal government should consider to increase the resilience of communities and critical infrastructure include the following:

Ensure relevant Federal regulations, policies, and guidance demonstrate leadership on community adaptation

As communities rise to the challenge of adapting to climate change, Federal agencies should harmonize existing policies and adaptation efforts at the local, state, Tribal levels. Examples of proactive agency efforts include the following:

- DOT could assess the adequacy of transportation design standards, such as the "Greenbook,"[19] in light of future climate conditions;
- HUD, in coordination with DOE and EPA, could provide guidelines or update building codes for implementation of housing adaptation strategies that address low- and moderate-income housing among other changing housing needs;
- NOAA could expand the development of tools, services, and training which provide guidance on adaptation in coastal communities;
- EPA could establish approaches for integrating projected climate change impacts into drainage risk management and the design and management of drinking and waste water treatment plants;
- USACE could provide climate change guidance for flood and storm risk management plans; and
- FEMA could update its flood insurance maps to reflect climate change.

State, Tribal, and local representatives, through improved partnerships with the federal government (See Goal 5), will play an important role in informing these Federal efforts.

Integrate adaptation considerations into Federal programs that affect communities

The Federal agencies should coordinate planning processes and programs that determine Federal investments in housing, transportation, environmental protection, and hazard mitigation in metropolitan areas. They should also integrate adaptation measures into these processes and programs. To facilitate interagency cooperation on community adaptation, grant programs could be jointly issued or reviewed by multiple agencies. Coordination could be supported through an interagency Memorandum of Understanding or by designating an entity to oversee coordination (e.g., CEQ, a workgroup under USGCRP, or the White House Office of Urban Affairs). One example of successful interagency coordination to assist communities is the Partnership for Sustainable Communities, a joint collaboration of DOT, HUD, and EPA. Additionally, agencies such as EPA, HUD, DOT, NOAA, and DOE that have existing programs focused on community resilience should work collaboratively in conducting pilot projects to deliver direct technical assistance to individual communities that can then serve as models for other areas.

Recommended Action: Facilitate the incorporation of climate change into insurance mechanisms

The effects of climate change are already clearly understood by public and private insurers. At the Federal level, two major public insurance programs are already affected by climate change and will require adaptive actions:

- FEMA, within the Department of Homeland Security (DHS), administers the NFIP which enables property owners in participating communities to purchase insurance protection against losses from flooding.
- The Risk Management Agency, within USDA, administers the Federal Crop Insurance Corporation, which provides crop insurance to farmers.

Private insurers investing in climate-vulnerable industries are already experiencing greater losses. This is affecting the availability and affordability of insurance. Insurance markets may have insufficient capital to cover increasing catastrophic losses, especially if rates cannot track climate risks.

When accurately priced to reflect risk, insurance can provide an important signal to customers (including homeowners, farmers, coastal communities, and businesses) and create incentives for adaptation. However, inaccurate pricing signals, including those that do not incorporate climate risk, can hinder effective adaptation. When considering insurance policy, it is also important to recognize that disaster insurance provides an important safety net for low-income and minority populations, whose residential options are sometimes limited and who may lack the means to relocate.

Explore a public/private partnership initiative to produce an open-source risk assessment model

Current risk assessment modeling for the insurance sector is characterized by limited capacity among stakeholders, uncoordinated spending on models, and a lack of transparency. Insurers, reinsurers, and state and non-governmental representatives agree that there is an opportunity to partner with the federal government on modeling to address these concerns.

An open-source community model addressing the risk of catastrophic events (such as coastal storms) and persistent and sub-catastrophic events (e.g., droughts, wildfires, and floods) in a defined geographic area across residential and commercial sectors (e.g., energy, water, transportation) will foster improved data quality and sharing, create more realistic risk-based pricing signals for public and private insurance, and create public awareness. The opening step for this initiative is a feasibility study to assess project requirements and outcomes, followed by initial design or scoping of a model. This initiative is related to and complements findings identified by two recent government-wide efforts.[20,21]

Recommended Action: Address additional cross-cutting issues

The Task Force recognizes that a National approach to adaptation will need to consider additional cross-cutting issues. The Task Force selected the cross-cutting issues discussed above based on existing interest and capacity for interagency dialogue. The Task Force has identified two additional areas that cut across sectors and agencies for further study in the near term, recognizing that there are many high priority sectors that will ultimately need to be addressed:

- Coastal and ocean resilience; and
- Fish, wildlife, and plant resources and their habitats.

In the past year, the Obama Administration and Congress also recognized the importance of these two cross-cutting adaptation issues through an Executive Order and legislation, respectively. Interagency efforts to address these issues are already underway and can both inform and learn from the ongoing work of the Task Force. In addition to coordinating with and supporting these initiatives, the Task Force will continue to identify other cross-cutting issues (e.g., energy, agriculture, infrastructure) and prioritize those to address.

Over the next year, the federal government should work to:

Develop a strategic action plan focused on strengthening the resilience of coastal, ocean and Great Lakes communities and ecosystems to climate change

Coastal and ocean environments both influence and are affected by a changing climate. The global ocean influences the Earth's climate and climate variability, while coastal and ocean environments are vulnerable to climate change impacts including sea level rise, increased severe storm events, erosion, water supply issues, and ocean acidification. These impacts will affect human populations, infrastructure, ecosystems, and biological diversity, as well as the valuable ecosystem services provided by the nation's oceans, Great Lakes, and coasts.

On July 19, 2010, President Obama signed an Executive Order establishing a National Ocean Policy that adopted the *Final Recommendations of the Interagency Ocean Policy Task Force.*[22] Acknowledging the vulnerability of ocean and coastal resources to climate change, one of the nine priority objectives for improving coastal and ocean stewardship the *Final Recommendations* identify is to "strengthen resiliency of coastal communities and marine and Great Lakes environments and their abilities to adapt to climate change impacts and ocean acidification." Under the Executive Order, the interagency National Ocean Council is tasked with developing strategic action plans for each priority objective within one year. Per the *Final Recommendations*, strategies will be developed to reduce the vulnerability, increase the resilience, and improve the adaptation of human and natural systems to climate change impacts.

The Task Force supports this effort, and recommends that the Interagency Policy Committee and planning effort include the appropriate expertise and input from local, state, Tribal, and Federal governmental and non-governmental partners. As noted above, this work should be coordinated with the development of a national action plan to support adaptation of freshwater resources to a changing climate, where appropriate. The National Ocean Council and the Task Force should coordinate with one another on a periodic basis to share progress and findings.

Develop a strategy for reducing the impacts of climate change on the nation's fish, wildlife, and plant resources and their habitats

It is clear that effective adaptation to climate change within the United States will depend on reducing the vulnerability and increasing the resilience of ecosystems, through adopting ecosystem-based adaptation strategies that focus on the continual provision of essential ecosystem services such as water supply, coastal protection, and carbon sequestration. Achieving this goal requires collaboration among the federal government, states, Tribes, non-governmental organizations, private industry, and private landowners to work together in new, expanded, and interdependent ways to successfully help species, habitats, and the communities and economies that depend on them adapt to a changing climate.

In the Fiscal Year 2010 Appropriations Act, Congress specifically called for the development of a National Fish, Wildlife, and Plants Climate Adaptation Strategy (NFWPCAS) by 2012. CEQ and DOI (with the USFWS as lead) were tasked to develop a national, Government-wide strategy that provides a unified approach–reflecting shared principles and science-based practices–for action by governmental and non-governmental organizations to reduce the impacts of climate change on the nation's species, habitats and ecological processes. The USFWS, working with a number of other agencies, has already taken several steps to begin developing the Strategy including drafting NFWPCAS Purpose, Vision, Guiding Principles, and Key Components documents, and holding eight listening sessions to seek input from stakeholders and the public.

Ecosystem- based adaptation strategies, such as protecting coastal wetlands to reduce damages from flooding, can improve resilience to climate change.

The Task Force supports CEQ and USFWS's efforts to develop the NFWPCAS, and recommends that a formal process be established, including the formation of a steering committee or workgroup, as appropriate, to draw on expertise and input from state, Tribal, and Federal governments and non-governmental partners in its development. This group and the Task Force should coordinate on a periodic basis to share progress and findings. Since the NFWPCAS will address adaptation of species and habitats in terrestrial, freshwater, coastal, and near-shore marine environments, development of the strategy should be coordinated with the National Ocean Council priority objective on coastal, ocean and Great Lakes resiliency and adaptation to climate change and ocean acidification.

Goal 4: Enhance Efforts to Lead and Support International Adaptation

Climate change poses particularly challenging risks and opportunities that are important to many of the U.S. Government's international development, security, and diplomatic priorities. Addressing climate change is one of the Administration's priority development initiatives and supports the President's new Global Development Policy. Developing countries are disproportionately affected by climate change because they are the most vulnerable and least able to cope with changing climate conditions and extreme weather events. Climate change also magnifies or contributes to other global development challenges, such as water, food, and energy security, public health, and biodiversity protection, among others. From a national security perspective, climate change may act as an "accelerant of instability or conflict."[23]

Climate change vulnerability is increasingly a political priority for many developing countries, a trend that is likely to continue as climate impacts become more acute. Adaptation is a key component of the December 2009 Copenhagen Accord and will continue to be an integral part of the global climate change negotiations. The United States has an opportunity to provide leadership for this emerging development and foreign policy issue. The Administration has placed renewed emphasis on climate change in its foreign assistance programs, and is working to integrate climate adaptation planning into a range of relevant development activities. Adaptation is one of three core "pillars" of the Administration's international climate budget.[24]

The United States should adopt an integrated and long-term approach that leverages the full technical capacities of the federal government to demonstrate leadership on international adaptation as this issue gains greater prominence in coming years. In particular, the federal government should build on existing adaptation programs and practices to: develop a Government-wide strategy for supporting multilateral and bilateral adaptation activities and integrating climate change adaptation into relevant U.S. foreign assistance and international activities; improve coordination and collaboration among international development, national security, and technical support agencies; and strengthen engagement with global partners to stimulate knowledge sharing and innovation, coordinate investments, and leverage local expertise and knowledge.

Recommended Action: Develop a Government-wide strategy to support multilateral and bilateral adaptation activities and integrate adaptation into relevant U.S. foreign assistance programs

The Administration has worked to develop an appropriate mix of multilateral and bilateral funding toward the United States' contribution to meet the financing commitments made by developed countries in Copenhagen. It has also taken steps to prioritize vulnerable countries and populations and to promote the integration of adaptation into broader development activities. These efforts are focused on improving the dissemination of information to help identify the greatest vulnerabilities to climate change, helping developing countries create governance systems that are inclusive, transparent, and responsive to the needs of their constituents, and implementing climate solutions that are locally appropriate and increase the resiliency of the world's most vulnerable populations.

Prolonged droughts due to climate change will impact global food security.

The Department of State, USAID, and Department of the Treasury have developed substantial adaptation initiatives and are beginning to integrate adaptation planning into core development programs, such as the Administration's global hunger and food security initiative (Feed the Future). Several other agencies, such as the Millennium Challenge Corporation (MCC), USDA, DOE, EPA, USACE, USGS, USFWS, and NOAA provide important expertise and resources that complement or directly support core adaptation objectives. The Department of State, USAID, and Department of the Treasury, working closely with other relevant Federal agencies, should develop a Government-wide strategy that builds on and enhances on-going adaptation efforts, supports the core principles and objectives of the President's new Global Development Policy, and coordinates resources and expertise across the federal government to support international adaptation initiatives.

Specifically, strategic objectives should include investments that help developing countries strengthen their capacity to conduct risk and vulnerability assessments, improve environmental governance, and integrate adaptation planning into core economic development programs (e.g., infrastructure, agriculture, energy, health, natural resource management, tourism). A standard set of definitions, performance metrics, and reporting criteria should be developed to guide and track U.S. Government contributions to international adaptation, including both bilateral and multilateral investments. Integrated approaches that foster synergies between climate change adaptation and mitigation[25] should be encouraged, where possible.

Recommended Action: Enhance collaboration on adaptation among international development, national security, and technical support agencies

To support a government-wide strategy for international adaptation, agencies should enhance collaboration on global climate change issues to better leverage the expertise and resources available, such as those from NOAA, USDA, USGS, EPA, DOE, and others. These agencies, though largely domestically focused, provide critical expertise, science, technology, and other tools that can be used in an international context for development planning and national security analysis. Furthermore, many technical agencies are already engaged in international climate adaptation efforts through global partnerships such as the United Nations and the World Meteorological Organization. Historically, collaboration between development and technical agencies on international climate issues has been limited. Collaboration could be greatly improved by building greater awareness within and outside of the federal government of the full range of capabilities and resources that technical agencies can provide to support international adaptation. Development agencies are generally not aware of the full scope of technical and scientific services available elsewhere in the Government that could be utilized in an international context. Similarly, technical and scientific agencies do not have a complete understanding of the data and information needs that exist in the development and national security agencies. The Government Accountability Office (GAO) and OMB have done an initial survey of adaptation capabilities within the Government, but a more comprehensive survey focused specifically on international capabilities and needs should be considered to help promote better alignment between the producers and consumers of international climate information. Agencies should consider how to best make this information available to development practitioners and scientists within and outside the Government. One option is to provide this information through an online information clearinghouse such as that recommended under Policy Goal 2.

Further, the national security and development communities should coordinate adaptation and analytic efforts to enhance the federal government's ability to meet its development objectives and mitigate national security risks. While the development and national security communities have different missions, they are linked by a common interest in the stability and wellbeing of developing countries and their populations. They also have a common need for the expertise and resources available from technical agencies. Timely and appropriate exchange of information and analyses between the national security and development communities will help ensure the effectiveness of Federal efforts on international adaptation and can provide insights into security risks that may be magnified by climate change.

Recommended Action: Engage global development partners and the private sector to promote knowledge sharing and coordinate investments
The United States should enhance interaction and cooperation with global development partners and the private sector to promote improved knowledge-sharing and the scaling up and dissemination of best practices to help developing countries reduce their vulnerability to climate change. Given the need to meet a growing challenge with a finite set of resources, it is vital to coordinate and leverage investments where possible to maximize adaptation and development outcomes and ensure resources are directed toward the greatest needs and priorities.

In addition to bilateral assistance, the United States should continue to support adaptation through multilateral assistance programs, which allow the

United States to leverage the resources of other donors as well as help other countries learn from these efforts and promote best practices. The United States contributes significantly to international climate adaptation efforts through its leadership in the Intergovernmental Panel on Climate Change, the Global Framework for Climate Services, and the Global Earth Observation System of Systems. Furthermore, the United States is actively engaged with other key donors and international institutions to coordinate efforts, deepen communication, and synthesize lessons learned as the United States and others scale up adaptation efforts in vulnerable countries and communities around the world.

> *"We recommend the cross-sector use of ecosystem-based approaches to adaptation planning; not only for the benefit of wildlife and plants, but also in support of human and built environments. Ecosystem-based adaptation complements other man-made climate change responses by increasing the resilience of ecosystems so they can continue to provide the full suite of benefits people rely on such as simultaneously sustaining biodiversity. While certain hard infrastructure responses to climate change will be needed, it is clear that effective long-term adaptation to climate change will depend on reducing the vulnerability and increasing the resilience of ecosystems and their essential services."*
> – The Nature Conservancy, Hawai'i Chapter at the Hawaii public outreach meeting

The United States should also expand partnerships with the private sector. Leveraging the expertise, capabilities, and investments of the private sector mobilizes additional financial and technical resources that can help magnify the scope and impact of public sector investments. The Department of State Global Partnership Initiative and USAID's Global Development Alliance are actively working to strengthen public-private partnerships that tap into the expertise and leadership of the private sector to advance international adaptation objectives. For example, USAID and NASA have developed partnerships with private technology companies for satellite-based regional forecasting systems in Central America and Africa (known as "SERVIR") that can be used to assess future impacts of climate change.

The Global Development Alliance and the Global Partnership Initiative should continue to explore opportunities for public-private sector partnerships that help build adaptive capacity internationally and support U.S. global development priorities. Specifically, there are significant opportunities to work with the financial services sector to spur further innovation and development of international adaptation financing and risk management strategies, including micro-insurance products. The United States should also seek to scale up initiatives to improve global climate data and knowledge management systems that increase the consistency, quality, and availability of scientific information. Public-private partnerships can also be beneficial to improving public messaging and communication about the importance of adaptation. To that end, the federal government should be transparent, and proactive in providing timely and relevant information on its support of international adaptation to the public.

Goal 5: Coordinate Capabilities of the Federal Government to Support Adaptation

As described throughout this report, the federal government already invests resources to provide climate science and services, technical support, and training to inform adaptation efforts at all scales. During the past year, stakeholders at local, state, Tribal, and regional levels requested that the development and delivery of these resources be better integrated to provide more efficient and effective support for adaptive action at all scales. The federal government needs to improve coordination of its science, services, and assessments programs to better enable stakeholders to access and leverage these resources in order to support decisions that enhance the resilience of communities, ecosystems, and the economy. The ongoing alignment of these activities is critical to achieve desired adaptation outcomes, ensure efficient deployment of Government resources, and respond to the evolving needs of stakeholders.

The National Climate Assessment (NCA) provides a valuable opportunity to engage with stakeholders and partners nationally and internationally, identify gaps in the federal government's ability to support adaptation, and better align and coordinate Federal capabilities. The third NCA is currently being developed, including a new approach to provide a continuing mechanism for engaging communities and networks of stakeholders at the local, state, Tribal, and regional levels. These stakeholders will collaborate with the federal government to produce information on assessing climate change impacts, vulnerability, and the capacity to prepare and respond. These assessments will help to identify science and service needs for understanding and adapting to regional and sectoral climate risks. The next NCA report is due in June 2013, and this ongoing assessment process, required by the Global Change Research Act of 1990, could provide an iterative evaluation of progress in the nation's adaptation efforts, as well as an important mechanism for information exchange and engagement.

In addition, the Task Force has identified three actions to improve the responsiveness and effectiveness of Federal efforts by building partnerships, coordinating efforts at the regional scale, and continuously evaluating the success of the Federal government in supporting adaptation at the national scale.

Recommended Action: Build and maintain strong partnerships to increase responsiveness of Federal Government activities to support local, state, and Tribal needs

Maintaining an open dialogue between Federal and non-Federal decision makers is critical to successful adaptation planning and implementation. The Task Force should establish a partnership committee composed of local, state, Tribal, and federal government representatives to exchange information and views on adaptation needs. This committee will be tasked with identifying how agencies can best coordinate and engage with stakeholders on an ongoing basis, as the federal government continues to enhance its support of adaptation efforts at various scales. This committee will increase engagement with non-Federal partners and serve as a venue for discussing the implementation of Federal policy and actions on cross-cutting adaptation issues. The work of this committee over the next year will provide the foundation for sustained and robust dialogue to better leverage, coordinate, and support U.S. adaptation efforts in the future. In addition to this committee, the Task Force will continue to engage with other non-governmental, private sector, and community-based organizations and networks. Agencies on the Task Force will also engage in ongoing dialogues with non-Federal partners as they work to develop agency-specific adaptation plans, provide accessible information and tools, foster local-to-global collaboration, and address stakeholder needs.

Recommended Action: Develop regional climate change adaptation consortia among Federal agencies

Many Federal agencies have regional offices and programs through which they actively engage with extensive networks of partners at the local-to-regional scale. Harmonizing efforts at the regional scale benefits both decision makers and information providers by avoiding duplication of efforts and leveraging existing capabilities. Federal agencies that work at the regional scale should consider how the range of programmatic activities already underway, from outreach to data collection, and research to information dissemination, meet the needs of stakeholders in the region. These efforts should build off of and strengthen existing regional networks. In addition, they should be considered on a region-by-region basis, as vulnerabilities, cultures, and agency responsibilities can vary across regions. Regional coordination will foster collaboration on the many science and service activities emerging across Federal agencies. Furthermore, a regional emphasis will create opportunities for improving the accessibility of existing science as well as responding to evolving information needs.

> *"We have to bring the partners together. We have to bring the stakeholders together and perhaps at the Federal level there's a way to look at how monies flow to communities so we get out of our silos and talk to each other and begin to plan together."*
>
> – Dr. Kevin Sherin, Orange County Health Department, State of Florida at the Portland public outreach meeting

The potential benefits of regional adaptation consortia include the following:

- Allow the federal government to learn from the adaptation efforts of regions, states and communities across the country.
- Facilitate Federal/non-Federal partnerships to leverage the resources of existing institutions, organizations, and networks.
- Provide practitioners with better access to information and technical assistance to support adaptation efforts at local-to-regional levels.
- Streamline and integrate monitoring information on local-to-regional impacts of climate change and build online access for sharing this information in a consistent and accessible format.
- Support activities of the NCA.
- Provide opportunities to develop region-specific guidance in support of adaptation planning and implementation.
- Enhance coordination among the regional offices of Federal agencies in the context of their agency adaptation planning processes (i.e., Policy Goal 1).

- Support the preparation, implementation, and evaluation of state and local climate change adaptation plans.

Recommended Action: Establish performance metrics for evaluating Federal adaptation efforts

Regular evaluation of the federal government's adaptation efforts is critical to continuously refining and improving adaptive approaches. An iterative evaluation process will allow adaptation plans, priorities, and actions to be revised as necessary if desired outcomes are not being achieved or if undesired consequences are occurring. The development of metrics of success for adaptation efforts is complex and challenging. Therefore, the Task Force will engage a variety of groups, such as the proposed partnership committee and the new Adaptation Science and Research Element of the USGCRP to discuss options. These groups should focus on high-level goals and performance metrics that look across Federal adaptation efforts at interagency, national, and international scales. This effort will complement the agency-level goals and performance metrics that will be developed as part of the agency adaptation planning process (Policy Goal 1). Federal agencies should harmonize goals and metrics with other Federal strategic planning initiatives where appropriate.

PART EIGHT. NEXT STEPS: BUILDING A MORE RESILIENT NATION

Over the past year, the Task Force has developed a vision, guiding principles, and policy goals that will provide a foundation for the federal government's role in a national adaptation strategy. The recommendations in this document are intended to foster action toward a common agenda of building a more resilient nation. Achieving this goal requires the coordination and integration of both Federal and non-Federal efforts across multiple scales, sectors, and stakeholders.

To continue to make progress towards building national resilience to climate change, the federal government should begin to implement the recommendations in this report. Key next steps include:

- Implement adaptation planning within Federal agencies to consider and address climate change impacts on missions, operations, and programs.
- Strengthen interagency coordination to build a robust body of accessible science and tools to inform and support adaptation decisions.
- Enhance the Government's ability to support and implement adaptive actions for the cross-cutting issues discussed in this report, and address additional cross-cutting issues over the next year (including coastal and ocean resilience and fish, wildlife, and plants).
- Develop an international adaptation strategy that builds on and enhances ongoing efforts, supports the core principles and objectives of the President's new Global Development Policy, and coordinates resources and expertise across the federal government to support international adaptation initiatives.
- Improve coordination of Federal efforts at the regional level to create efficiencies in climate science and services and to meet local, state, and regional adaptation needs.
- Establish a partnership committee composed of local, state, and Tribal representatives to allow the Task Force to consult with critical partners as the federal government begins to implement the actions contained in this report.

- Develop methods for evaluating the effectiveness of Federal actions to increase national adaptive capacity and resilience, which will be critical for continuously refining and improving the Government's approach to adaptation.

The Task Force will continue to meet over the next year to maintain an interagency forum for discussing the federal government's adaptation approach and to monitor the implementation of recommended actions articulated in this report. The Task Force will prepare a progress report in October 2011 that documents the results of federal government adaptation efforts over the year and provides additional recommendations for refining the federal government's adaptation efforts, as appropriate.

Through the actions described in this report and the collective actions of stakeholders at all levels, we strive to be a nation that better understands, and is better prepared for, the impacts of a changing climate. Adaptation across all scales and sectors will enable us to reduce the risks and seize the opportunities presented by climate change. These efforts, in tandem with advancing efforts to manage greenhouse gas emissions, are initial steps in what must be a long-term, iterative, and collaborative approach to make our nation more resilient to a range of possible futures.

APPENDIX A. MEMBERS OF THE INTERAGENCY CLIMATE CHANGE ADAPTATION TASK FORCE

Co-Chairs

Nancy H. Sutley, Chair, Council on Environmental Quality
Jane Lubchenco, Administrator, National Oceanic and Atmospheric Administration
Shere Abbott, Associate Director for Environment, Office of Science and Technology Policy

Steering Committee

Ron Sims, Deputy Secretary, Department of Housing and Urban Development
David J. Hayes, Deputy Secretary, Department of the Interior
Jonathon Pershing, U.S. Deputy Special Envoy for Climate Change, Department of State
Bob Perciasepe, Deputy Administrator, Environmental Protection Agency
Craig Fugate, Administrator, Federal Emergency Management Agency
Sally Ericsson, Associate Director for Natural Resources Programs, Office of Management and Budget

Executive Office of the President

Council on Environmental Quality (CEQ)
Jason Bordoff, Associate Director for Energy and Climate Change
Maria Blair, Deputy Associate Director for Climate Change Adaptation

Office of Energy and Climate Change (OECC)
Heather Zichal, Deputy Assistant to the President for Energy & Climate Change
Joe Aldy, Special Assistant to the President (Energy and Environment)

Office of Science & Technology Policy (OSTP)
John Holdren, Director
Phil DeCola, Senior Policy Analyst
Diana DiEuliis, Assistant Director for Life Science
Kathy Jacobs, Assistant Director for Climate Adaptation and Assessment

National Security Staff (NSS)
Ed Fendley, Director for International Environmental Issues

Office of Management and Budget
Cass Sunstein, Counselor, Office of Information and Regulatory Affairs

Council of Economic Advisors
Cecilia Rouse, Member
Arik Levinson, Senior Economist

National Economic Council
Diana Farrell, Deputy Assistant to the President for Economic Policy

Departments

Agriculture (USDA)
James W. Miller, Undersecretary for Farm and Foreign Agricultural Services
William Hohenstein, Director of Global Change Program Office
Robert Bonnie, Senior Advisor to the Secretary for Environment and Climate
Commerce (DOC)
Tom Karl, Director, National Climate Data Center
Monica Medina, Senior Advisor to the Administrator, NOAA

Defense (DOD)
Michele Flournoy, Undersecretary of Defense for Policy

Dorothy Robyn, Deputy Undersecretary for Defense Installations and Environment
Joellen Darcy, Assistant Secretary for Civil Works, Department of the Army
Jeff Marqusee, Executive Director, The Environmental Security Technology Certification Program
Maureen Sullivan, Director, Environmental Management, Office of Secretary of Defense
Bob Pietrowsky, Director of Institute for Water Resources, USACE
Terrence ("Rock") Salt, Principal Deputy Assistant Secretary of the Army (Civil Works)

Education (DOEd)
Steven Robinson, Special Advisor to the Secretary
Glenn Cummings, Deputy Assistant Secretary, Vocational and Adult Education

Energy (DOE)
David Sandalow, Assistant Secretary for Policy & International Affairs
Rick Duke, Deputy Assistant Secretary for Climate Policy
Bob Marlay, Director Office of Climate Change Policy & Technology
Craig Zamuda, Senior Policy Advisor, Office of Climate Change Policy & Technology

Health and Human Services (HHS)
Howard Koh, Assistant Secretary for Health
John Balbus, Senior Advisor for Public Health, NIH
Howard Frumkin, Director, National Center for Environmental Health

Homeland Security (DHS)
Alice C. Hill, Senior Counselor to the Secretary
Dave Kaufman, Director of FEMA Office Policy and Program Analysis

Housing and Urban Development (HUD)
James Lopez, Senior Advisor to the Deputy Secretary

Interior (DOI)
Tom Armstrong, Senior Advisor on Climate Change to the Deputy Secretary of the Interior

State (DOS)
Trigg Talley, Director, Office of Global Change

Transportation (DOT)
Roy Kienitz, Undersecretary of Transportation for Policy
Kathryn Thomson, Counselor to the Secretary
Linda Lawson, Director, Office of Safety, Energy, and Environment

Treasury
Billy Pizer, Deputy Assistant Secretary for Environment and Energy

Independent Agencies

Agency for International Development (USAID)
Bill Breed, USAID Global Climate Change Team Leader

United States Environmental Protection Agency (EPA)
Lisa Heinzerling, Associate Administrator for Policy
Robert Verchick, Deputy Associate Administrator for Policy

National Aeronautics and Space Administration (NASA)
Michael Freilich, Director of Earth Science Division
Jack Kaye, Associate Director for Research, Earth Science Division

National Intelligence Council (NIC)
Rich Engel, Director, Climate Change and State Stability Program

Millennium Challenge Corporation (MCC)
Darius Teter, Deputy Vice President, Compact Operations
James Greene, Deputy Vice President, Policy and International Relations

Key Support Personnel

Council on Environmental Quality (CEQ)
Loren Labovitch, Climate Adaptation Manager
Allison Castellan, Climate Adaptation Analyst
Kim Penn, Climate Adaptation Analyst
Bill Perkins, Climate Adaptation Analyst

Seth Silverman, Climate Adaptation Analyst

APPENDIX B. WORKGROUPS OF THE INTERAGENCY CLIMATE CHANGE ADAPTATION TASK FORCE

Adaptation Science

National Oceanic and Atmospheric Administration*
Office of Science and Technology Policy*
American Association for the Advancement of Science
Bureau of Land Management
Centers for Disease Control
Council on Environmental Quality
Department of Agriculture
Department of Homeland Security
Department of Energy
Department of Defense
Department of State

Department of Transportation
Environmental Protection Agency
National Aeronautics and Space Administration
National Institute of Food and Agriculture
National Institutes of Health
National Science Foundation
USDA Forest Service
U.S. Army Corps of Engineers
U.S. Agency for International Development
U.S. Fish and Wildlife Service
U.S. Global Change Research Program
U.S. Geological Survey

Agency Adaptation Planning

Department of Housing and Urban Development*

---

* Designates workgroup co-chair.

Environmental Protection Agency*
Centers for Disease Control
Council of Economic Advisers
Council on Environmental Quality
Department of Homeland Security
Department of Defense
Department of Energy
Department of the Interior
Department of Transportation
Federal Emergency Management Agency
National Park Service
Office of the Chief Economist
Office of Federal Environmental Executive
Office of Management and Budget
U.S. Army Corps of Engineers
U.S. Agency for International Development
U.S. Department of Agriculture
U.S. Global Change Research Program
U.S. Geological Survey

Water Resources Adaptation

Council on Environmental Quality*
U.S. Geological Survey*
Environmental Protection Agency*
Centers for Disease Control
Department of Energy
Department of State
National Aeronautics and Space Administration
National Oceanic and Atmospheric Administration
National Park Service
National Science Foundation
Office of Science and Technology Policy
USDA Forest Service
U.S. Bureau of Reclamation
U.S. Army Corps of Engineers

---

* Designates workgroup co-chair.

U.S. Agency for International Development
U.S. Department of Agriculture
U.S. Global Change Research Program

Insurance Adaptation

Office of Management and Budget*
U.S. Army Corps of Engineers*
Department of Transportation*
Council of Economic Advisers
Council on Environmental Quality
Department of Homeland Security
Department of the Interior
Department of the Treasury
Federal Emergency Management Agency
National Oceanic and Atmospheric Administration
Office of the Chief Economist
Office of Science and Technology Policy
U.S. Agency for International Development
U.S. Department of Agriculture
U.S. Fish and Wildlife Service

International Resilience

Council on Environmental Quality*
U.S. Department of State*
U.S. Army Corps of Engineers*
Centers for Disease Control
Department of Defense
Department of Energy
Department of Homeland Security
Department of the Interior
Department of Transportation
Department of the Treasury
Environmental Protection Agency

---

* Designates workgroup co-chair.

Federal Emergency Management Agency
Millennium Challenge Corporation
National Aeronautics and Space Administration
National Intelligence Council
National Oceanic and Atmospheric Administration
National Security Staff
Office of Management and Budget
Office of Science and Technology Policy
U.S. Agency for International Development
U.S. Department of Agriculture
U.S. Fish and Wildlife Service
U.S. Global Change Research Program
U.S. Geological Survey

Communications and Outreach

Council on Environmental Quality*
Department of the Interior
Environmental Protection Agency
Federal Emergency Management Agency
National Oceanic and Atmospheric Administration
National Science Foundation
U.S. Department of Agriculture
U.S. Global Change Research Program
U.S. Geological Survey

Urban

Environmental Protection Agency*
Department of Transportation*
Council on Environmental Quality

---

* Designates workgroup co-chair.

Department of State
Federal Emergency Management Agency
Department of Housing and Urban Development
National Oceanic and Atmospheric Administration
U.S. Army Corps of Engineers

Health

Centers for Disease Control*
National Institutes of Health*
Council on Environmental Quality
Department of Defense
Department of Homeland Security
Department of the Interior
Environmental Protection Agency
National Oceanic and Atmospheric Administration
Office of Science and Technology Policy
Smithsonian Institute
U.S. Department of Agriculture
U.S. Global Change Research Program
U.S. Geological Survey

Plants, Fish, Wildlife

U.S. Fish and Wildlife Service*
Council on Environmental Quality
National Oceanic and Atmospheric Administration
Office of Management and Budget
USDA Forest Service
U.S. Army Corps of Engineers
U.S. Department of Agriculture

---

* Designates workgroup co-chair.

APPENDIX C. SUMMARY OF PUBLIC OUTREACH EFFORTS OF THE INTERAGENCY CLIMATE CHANGE ADAPTATION TASK FORCE

Major public outreach meetings of the Task Force[26]

- Health, Portland (sponsored by CDC) – June 6, 2010
- Hazard Preparedness, Miami (sponsored by FEMA, NOAA) – June 23, 2010
- Island Resilience, Honolulu (sponsored by DOI, NOAA) – July 9, 2010
- Urban and Ecosystems, Chicago (sponsored by EPA, HUD) – July 15, 2010
- Agriculture, Denver (sponsored by USDA) – July 19, 2010

Workgroup-sponsored listening sessions (25 sessions)

Urban Workgroup
- Urban Adaptation Issues #1 – May 5, 2010
- Urban Adaptation Issues #2 – May 12, 2010

Science Workgroup
- Adaptation Science and Cities – October 29, 2009
- Adaptation Science and States – November 5, 2009
- Adaptation Science and Planners, Resource Managers, and Decision makers – November 12, 2009
- Science regional case, Gulf Coast #1 – April 8, 2010
  (Incorporating Climate Change into Decision Making and Planning)
- Science regional case, Gulf Coast #2 – April 15, 2010
  (Climate Information Needs for the Transportation Sector (Phase II of DOT study)
- Science regional case, Gulf Coast #3 – April 23, 2010
  (Building Ecosystem Resilience to Climate Change)

Water Adaptation Workgroup
- Energy and Industrial Organizations – October 27, 2009
- State, Tribal and Water Utility Organizations – October 28, 2009

- Environmental and Coastal Organizations – October 28, 2009
- Agriculture and Transportation Organizations – November 2, 2009
- Public Health Organizations – December 1, 2009

International Adaptation Workgroup
- Development Assistance and Humanitarian Relief Organizations – November 6, 2009
- National Security Organizations – November 9, 2009
- Private sector businesses – November 12, 2009

Agency Adaptation Workgroup
- National Governments – October 26, 2009
- National Governments, II – October 27, 2009
- Local Governments – November 6, 2009
- State Governments – November 16, 2009
- Tribes – November 16, 2009

Insurance Adaptation Workgroup
- Industry Perspectives – November 4, 2009
- Commissioner Perspectives – November 10 , 2009
- Academic Perspectives – November 19, 2009

Health Workgroup
- Health Adaptation – April 30, 2010

Other outreach events, workshops, and meetings

- Special Adaptation Session during the Native Peoples Native Homelands Tribal Climate Change Conference (www.nativepeoples nativehomelands.org) – November 19, 2009, Minnesota
- Science Translation Workshop – April 30, 2010, Washington, D.C.
- National Adaptation Summit – May 19, 2010, Washington, D.C.
- Institute for Sustainable Communities/CCAP listening session with non-Federal partners – June 16, 2010
- Private Sector Focus Group on International Climate Adaptation and Resilience – June 21, 2010, Washington D.C.

APPENDIX D. SUMMARY OF PUBLIC COMMENTS RECEIVED ON THE INTERAGENCY CLIMATE CHANGE ADAPTATION TASK FORCE INTERIM PROGRESS REPORT

The Task Force received over 27,000 public comments regarding its March 16, 2010 Interim Progress Report[27]. Comments were submitted to CEQ's public website. Comments were received from a variety of stakeholders including environmental advocacy groups, private industry, government representatives, and the general public. Of the total comments received, approximately 25,000 were "mass mailers" (form letters) from members of non-profit organizations. The great majority of the comments were positive and supported the Task Force's efforts on adaptation, though there were some comments that expressed skepticism about climate change and the need to adapt. Some common themes among the comments received are summarized below (in no particular order):

- **Broad stakeholder engagement is necessary** – many groups were concerned that there was not enough stakeholder engagement thus far, and they wanted to see a process moving forward that would incorporate stakeholder feedback, especially that of vulnerable populations. Additionally, many of the groups are interested in further engagement with the Task Force.
- **Coordination and collaboration is necessary between all levels of government and stakeholders** – many groups commented that the current coordination and collaboration efforts are lacking, and they wanted to see a process moving forward that would provide a coordination mechanism.
- **Funding at the local/State level is needed** – many groups commented that adaptation actions will largely be taken at the local level and that sustained funding would be necessary to support those actions.
- **Supportive of Federal guidance and leadership** – while most adaptation actions occur at the local level, many people suggested that more Federal guidance and leadership is needed.
- **Improve accessibility of science through creating an information clearinghouse for decision makers at many scales** – in order for policy makers at all levels of government to make sustainable long-

term decisions, groups asked for a single place to gather information, and provide that information in way that is usable.

- **Include end-users of scientific information in the decision making process** – these users must be engaged in the shaping of Federal research programs.
- **A national strategy should be flexible and scalable** – the national strategy should be responsive to the needs and priorities of stakeholders and be able to be adjusted as those needs change.
- **Prioritization and evaluation methods are essential** – many groups expressed that prioritization was needed from the Federal level, especially for help with local actions and funding. Additionally, many groups were interested in an evaluation component that could gauge the effectiveness of adaptation actions.
- **Ecosystem-based approaches should be pursued for adaptation** – many of the groups stressed that ecosystem-based approaches to adaptation were no-regret solutions that would help build sustainability and resiliency.
- **Support for review of existing regulations and policies** – many groups expressed the need for decision makers to review existing policies and regulations to ensure that they did not inadvertently increase vulnerability to climate change.

APPENDIX E. SUMMARIES OF THE TASK FORCE'S PUBLIC OUTREACH MEETINGS

Summary of CDC Public Outreach Meeting (June 6, 2010 in Portland, OR[28])

Background: This outreach meeting was organized by CDC on behalf of the Task Force. It was held in conjunction with the annual meeting of the Council of State and Territorial Epidemiologists as an evening keynote session. Objectives for the meeting included:

- To discuss the likely range of climate change impacts to public health and the need for adaptation strategies to reduce vulnerability and increase resilience;

- To inform stakeholders at all levels about the work of the Task Force, as well as public health adaptation efforts underway at the Federal level; and
- To provide an opportunity for the Task Force to listen to state and local public health officials describe efforts already underway to plan for climate change, as well as their needs and challenges.

Participation and Agenda: Speakers included Task Force members as well as State and local health officials. The session focused around an expert panel on public health adaptation. In addition, diverse stakeholders (e.g., local and State governments, non-governmental organizations, and private citizens) provided input during the public comment period.

Outcome and Findings: The outreach meeting provided an excellent opportunity for information sharing between the federal government and its local and regional partners on adaptation. The following key messages, themes, and recommendations relevant to adaptation emerged during the panel discussions and public comment period:

- Enhanced surveillance is needed on the public health impacts of climate change, including measurement of additional indicators.
- The federal government should ensure that there is a collaborative and cohesive Federal response to climate change.
- Adaptation efforts must address vulnerable populations and incorporate efforts to reduce existing health inequities that will be exacerbated by climate change.
- There can be significant public health benefits from mitigation actions, and these should be better communicated to the public.
- Public health stakeholders need to be brought together to plan for climate change.
- Better urban planning and design can increase community resilience.
- There is a need for stronger communication in general on climate change health impacts, e.g., heat waves.

Summary of NOAA/FEMA Public Outreach Meeting (June 23, 2010 in Miami, FL)

Background: This listening session was organized by NOAA and FEMA on behalf of the Task Force. Objectives for the session included:

- To discuss the likely range of coastal climate change impacts and the growing need for adaptation strategies to ensure community resilience;
- To inform stakeholders at all levels about how communities are preparing for and responding to climate change impacts; and
- To provide an opportunity for the Task Force to listen to local and regional decision makers, managers, and planners describe efforts already underway to plan for climate change, as well as their needs and challenges.

Participation and Agenda: Speakers included Obama Administration officials, Task Force members, and local and regional scientists, elected officials, agency personnel, and ecosystem managers. The session included two panels:

- Hazard preparedness and climate change adaptation; and
- Water resource management and downstream implications for the Everglades.

In addition, diverse stakeholders (e.g, non-governmental organizations, local governments, private citizens) provided input during public comment periods. A press conference followed.

Outcome and Findings: The listening session provided an excellent opportunity for information sharing between the federal government and its local and regional partners on adaptation. The following key messages, themes, and recommendations relevant to adaptation emerged:

- Climate change needs to be integrated into existing and emerging plans and operations.
- Support and expand partnerships between the Federal government and its local partners on climate change adaptation; build on existing successful local-Federal partnerships (e.g., NOAA's Digital Coasts tool for planning efforts in South Florida).
- Public education and risk communication are important for building understanding.
- Disaster planning is a form of climate change adaptation, and communities already plan for disasters; we can learn from these efforts as we build a "risk-smart future."
- Community resilience depends on ecosystem resilience. South Florida is an excellent case study for emphasizing the importance of ecosystem-based adaptation; restoring the Everglades ecosystem will buffer the urban communities from climate change impacts.
- The federal government can facilitate adaptation by providing technical assistance, tools, information, and financial resources to its partners.
- Accessible science and tools are needed to support adaptation decisions. Scientific priorities discussed include:
  - Conduct risk and vulnerability assessments at local-to-regional scales
  - Improve climate change projections at the regional scale o Reduce uncertainty of sea level rise projections
  - Develop communication and decision-support tools (e.g., visualization, valuation)
- An effective mantra for adaptation is: "Think globally, work regionally, act locally."

Summary of NOAA/DOI Public Outreach Meeting (July 9, 2010 in Honolulu, HI)

Background: This public outreach meeting was organized by NOAA and DOI on behalf of the Task Force. Objectives for the session included:

- To discuss the likely range of coastal climate change impacts and the growing need for adaptation strategies to ensure island community resilience;

- To inform stakeholders at all levels about how communities are preparing for and responding to climate change impacts; and
- To provide an opportunity for the Task Force to listen to local and regional decision makers, managers, and planners describe efforts already underway to plan for climate change, as well as their needs and challenges.

Participation and Agenda: Speakers included Obama Administration officials, Task Force members, and local and regional scientists, elected officials, agency personnel, and ecosystem managers. The session focused on an expert panel that discussed different facets of island resiliency in the face of climate change. In addition, diverse stakeholders (e.g., non-governmental organizations, local governments, private citizens) provided input during public comment periods.

Outcome and Findings: The listening session provided an excellent opportunity for information sharing between the federal government and its local and regional partners on adaptation. The following key messages, themes, and recommendations relevant to adaptation emerged:

- Climate mitigation and adaptation in the islands is not a long-term strategy, they must happen now and they should both be pursued.
- Adaptation (and mitigation) investments should include enhanced education and literacy programs and targeted opportunities to engage and empower youth.
- Support and expand partnerships between the federal government and its local partners on climate change adaptation; build on existing successful local-Federal partnerships.
- Migration from islands should be considered with climate adaptation, and there is a potential need for a national migration strategy.
- Community resilience depends on ecosystem resilience. There is a need for research and stable funding for natural resource adaptation.
- The federal government can facilitate adaptation by providing technical assistance, tools, information, and financial resources to its partners including alternative energy development.
- In climate adaptation planning there should be a cultural component to decision making.

- In the Pacific Islands, climate change impacts will drive competition for both land and water, and adaptation plans incorporating them should be a priority.

Summary of EPA/HUD Public Outreach Meeting (July 15, 2010 in Chicago, IL)

Background: This public outreach meeting was organized by EPA and HUD on behalf of the Task Force. Objectives for this session included:

- To discuss the likely range of climate change impacts on the Great Lakes region and the growing need for adaptation strategies to ensure healthy economies and ecosystems;
- To inform stakeholders and public about the Task Force as well as adaptation efforts underway at the Federal level; and
- To provide an opportunity for the Task Force to listen to local and regional experts describe adaptation efforts underway in the Great Lakes region and their needs and challenges.

Participation and Agenda: Speakers included Task Force members, local and regional scientists, Federal and local decision makers, and non-governmental representatives. The session included two panels: (1) Great Lakes Ecosystem Adaptation; and (2) Urban Infrastructure Adaptation. In addition, diverse stakeholders (i.e., local and State governments, non-governmental organizations, and private citizens) provided input during public comment periods.

Outcome and Findings: The session provided an excellent opportunity for information sharing between the federal government and regional partners on adaptation. The following key themes and recommendations emerged during the panel and public comment sessions:

- An ecosystem-based approach to adaptation is critical. The Great Lakes Restoration Initiative is a good model for how Federal agencies can work across sectors.

- Adaptation actions need to have a strong monitoring component. Federal guidance on monitoring is important in order to compare different adaptation approaches.
- The federal government needs to facilitate local adaptation through encouragement, regulation, and financial and technical assistance. Priorities discussed included:
  - Region-specific, downscaled climate projections, especially of storm intensity
  - Tools and support for conducting vulnerability and risk assessments
  - Science translators based in communities (e.g., extension model)
  - Analyses of the economic benefits of adaptation (or costs of inaction)
  - Opportunities for sharing lessons learned
- We don't always need new resources; we just need to realign existing resources more effectively. Adaptation needs to be integrated into existing activities, and adaptation actions that also have mitigation benefits need to be prioritized.
- The federal government has a key role in adaptation messaging to ensure a consistent message across the Government. The public needs to understand climate science is sound.
- Water resources and urban areas are two of the most critical focus points for adaptation. Most of the population lives in urban areas and water drives many other issues (e.g., health, agriculture, energy, etc.).

Summary of USDA Public Outreach Meeting (July 19, 2010 in Denver, CO)

Background: This public outreach meeting was organized by USDA on behalf of the Task Force. The Task Force meeting was held as part of an all-day event hosted by USDA on Helping Agriculture Adapt to a Changing Climate. The morning session of the USDA event focused on the latest science related to climate change and agriculture and provided case studies of how farmers are being affected by climate change. Objectives for this session included:

- To discuss the likely range of climate change impacts on the agriculture sector and the growing need for adaptation strategies to ensure food security, robust rural economies, and healthy ecosystems.
- To inform stakeholders and public about the Task Force as well as adaptation efforts underway at the Federal level; and
- To provide an opportunity for the Task Force to listen to farmers and stakeholders as well as local and regional experts describe the need for adaptation efforts especially in the agriculture sector.

Participation and Agenda: Speakers included Task Force members, farmers and representatives of farm organizations, and scientists. The session included two panels: (1) Administration Strategy; and (2) Reactions from Agriculture. In addition, diverse stakeholders (i.e., Tribal governments, nongovernmental organizations, and private citizens) provided input during public comment period.

Outcome and Findings: The meeting offered insight into the risks and vulnerabilities of the agriculture sector to climate change and priorities for Federal responses. The following key themes and recommendations emerged during the panel and public comment sessions:

- Farmers and ranchers have experience in understanding and managing risks. However, climate change may pose new risks that will require new management strategies.
- Farmers have many questions about the rate and nature of climate change, expected impacts and risks, and adaptation strategies.
- The risks to agriculture are widespread and include: changes to winter snowpack, extreme temperatures during grain set and pollination, fewer cooling degree days for setting deciduous tree fruits, changes to pest and disease outbreaks, and increases in extreme weather events. These impacts vary by region.
- Farmers rely on a number of Federal programs for information and assistance in managing their lands. These programs could be leveraged to educate and inform farmers and ranchers about climate change and to help them manage risks. Examples include: crop insurance, extension, and conservation programs.

- Although climate change is a long-term phenomenon, actions must begin soon to help agriculture adapt. These adaptation measures will have costs.
- Development of new plants and production practices may take years to perfect, and there are numerous crops (in particular specialty crops) that might be affected.
- The federal government will need to continue to focus on research to help farmers adapt to climate change, including developing new drought- and salinity-tolerant varieties, pest and disease eradication tools, systems to improve irrigation efficiency, and improved water storage capacity for agricultural uses.
- To be fully successful, farmers will need technical assistance from the federal government and practical guidance on adaptation strategies.
- Natural resource inventories and data systems should be used to monitor and track the impacts of climate change on land systems.

APPENDIX F. NATIONAL CLIMATE ADAPTATION SUMMIT REPORT EXECUTIVE SUMMARY

The National Climate Adaptation Summit was in response to a conversation the President's Science and Technology Advisor, Dr. John Holdren, had with the University Corporation for Atmospheric Research (UCAR) Board members and took place in Washington, DC, on May 25-27, 2010. This event brought together more than 180 users and providers of climate adaptation information to examine the needs, knowledge, and roles required for effective adaptation to climate change. The goal of the Summit was to inform Federal, state, regional, and local climate adaptation efforts, including the planning of the Federal Interagency Climate Change Adaptation Task Force and the U.S. Global Change Research Program.

There was a strong consensus among participants that wise adaptation measures can help minimize the negative impacts of a changing climate on our nation's communities, businesses, ecosystems, and citizens. Effective adaptation will require improved coordination within agencies and among agencies, states, regions and the private sector. It also calls for new methods of communication; sharing of best practices; budget increases in a few key areas; research to produce needed missing information; development of new partnerships; and 'learning by doing', or *adaptive* adaptation.

The Summit identified seven priorities for near-term action:

- **Developing an overarching national strategy to guide federal climate change adaptation programs.** This strategy should establish agency roles, clear goals and metrics, and better mechanisms for coordinating federal and non-federal activities.
- **Improving coordination of Federal plans and programs.** Strong management from the executive branch is needed to break down barriers, integrate planning, move funding into the highest priority areas, and maintain priorities across the multitude of involved agencies.
- **Creating a Federal climate information portal.** This would provide single-point access to data from all relevant Federal agencies and programs and would evolve over time into a more "national" portal with information about relevant non-Federal efforts.
- **Creating a clearinghouse of best practices and toolkits for adaptation.** Such an effort could assist regions and sectors with similar adaptation challenges in learning from each other and explore the intersection of adaptation and mitigation.
- **Including support for assessment in USGCRP agency budgets.** This would enable the regular national-scale assessments of climate change impacts that are required by law.
- **Increasing funding for research on vulnerability and impacts, including economic analyses, and pilot projects that join local, state, and regional governments and academic institutions to develop and test adaptation measures and tools.**
- **Initiating a regional series of ongoing climate adaptation forums.** The goal would be to integrate planning, communication, and coordination of activities across various agencies and U.S. regions.

APPENDIX G. ONGOING PILOT PROJECTS USING THE FLEXIBLE FRAMEWORK FOR ADAPTATION PLANNING

U.S. Army Corps of Engineers Pilots (Project-Level)

Project-level pilots under the USACE Responses to Climate Change Program are actively using the flexible framework approach to climate change adaptation and resilience developed by the Task Force. Pilot projects include evaluations of multipurpose reservoir operations related to flood risk reduction, an ecosystem restoration project (complete), two planning studies affected by sea level change, an interagency (USACE-Reclamation) paired basin study evaluating the effects of climate change on sedimentation, and an interagency project addressing drought for a multipurpose reservoir impacting interstate water supply, among other purposes. Additional pilots will be conducted over the next year. To date, these pilots demonstrate that the flexible framework works well as an organizing tool and can be applied with good effect to existing USACE projects.

Department of Homeland Security Pilot (Agency-Wide)

DHS used the flexible framework to engage in an extended agency-wide adaptation planning exercise across all components. DHS determined it needed to take a proactive approach to climate adaptation in order to deliver on its missions set forth in the 2010 Quadrennial Homeland Security Review. As a collaborative, department-wide initiative, the project aimed to: raise awareness of impacts of climate change and risks to DHS mission and operations; identify and prioritize major impacts of climate change and risks to DHS; identify potential adaptation strategies; make recommendations for incorporating climate change adaptation into ongoing Departmental planning processes; and develop partnerships with other agencies, businesses and research institutions to leverage scientific/technical expertise and support future work. The pilot produced a report that will be provided to the DHS Secretary that includes a summary of Task Force activities and analysis of key risks identified in case study regions as well as potential recommendations for how DHS should address climate change moving forward.

Department of Transportation Pilot (Agency Component, State-wide)

Recognizing that FHWA must include climate change in its risk and vulnerability assessments of transportation infrastructure, DOT/FHWA set out to help transportation decision makers, particularly transportation planners, asset managers, and system operators, identify which infrastructure assets (a) are most exposed to the threats from climate change and/or (b) could result in the most serious consequences as a result of those threats. DOT/FHWA has developed a vulnerability tool for state and municipal planners that takes a deeper look at steps in the flexible framework for understanding climate risk and applying that risk to mission and activities. DOT/FHWA is piloting this conceptual model among three to four State Departments of Transportation or Metropolitan Planning Organizations.

EPA Pilot (Community-level)

EPA is working in Iowa to identify barriers to and incentives for considering regional effects of climate change in hazard mitigation and other community planning processes. Several organizations are working to support resilient, sustainable communities in Iowa which are experiencing floods that are growing more severe and frequent. Communities in Iowa engage in multiple planning activities, including hazard mitigation planning and comprehensive or community planning, that can help guide them as they try to become more resilient to the effects of climate change. Iowa's recently passed smart planning legislation and its component smart planning principles can also help communities put plans in place that include adaptation strategies. Climate change information will be important to both risk assessment and community recovery decisions. This pilot will explore if and how climate change information should be considered in risk assessment and the implications this information may have for community planning options. This pilot has sought approaches with mutual benefits and synergies across planning requirements and has emphasized the need to work across agencies and levels of government to optimize results.

End Notes

[1] *Global Climate Change Impacts in the United States*, Karl, Thomas R., Melillo, Jerry M., Peterson, Thomas C. (eds.). Cambridge University Press (2009).

[2] The Global Change Research Act of 1990 established the U.S. Global Change Research Program to provide "...coordination of a comprehensive and integrated U.S. research program which will assist the nation and the world to understand, assess, predict, and respond to human-induced and natural processes of global change." Thirteen Federal agencies contribute a total of $2.1B (FY2010) toward the program.

[3] *Global Climate Change Impacts in the United States*, Karl, Thomas R., Melillo, Jerry M., Peterson, Thomas C., (2009).

[4] *Climate Change 2007: Impacts, Adaptation and Vulnerability*, Parry, M.L., Canziani, O. F., Palutikof, J. P., van der Linden, P. J., et. al., contribution of Working Group II to the Fourth Assessment Report of the Intergovernmental Panel on Climate Change 2007 (2007).

[5] *Global Climate Change Impacts in the United States*, Karl, Thomas R., Melillo, Jerry M., Peterson, Thomas C., (2009).

[6] *Advancing the Science of Climate Change*, America's Climate Choices: Panel on Advancing the Science of Climate Change, National Research Council, (2010).

[7] *Global Climate Change Impacts in the United States*, Karl, Thomas R., Melillo, Jerry M., Peterson, Thomas C., (2009).

[8] *Ibid.*

[9] *Ibid.*

[10] *Ibid.*

[11] *Ibid.*

[12] *Ibid.*

[13] Details of these projects are provided in Appendix G.

[14] While the Urban Workgroup originally focused on urban issues, the Task Force recognized that the recommendations they developed were broadly applicable to all communities.

[15] *Global Climate Change Impacts in the United States*, Karl, Thomas R., Melillo, Jerry M., Peterson, Thomas C., (2009).

[16] *Climate Change 2007: Impacts, Adaptation and Vulnerability*, Parry, M.L., Canziani, O. F., Palutik of, J. P., vander Linden, P. J., et. al., contribution of Working Group II to the Fourth Assessment Report of the Intergovernmental Panel on Climate Change 2007 (2007).

[17] *Global Climate Change Impacts in the United States*, Karl, Thomas R., Melillo, Jerry M., Peterson, Thomas C., (2009).

[18] *Climate Change 2007: Impacts, Adaptation and Vulnerability*, Parry, M.L., Canziani, O. F., Palutikof, J. P., vander Linden, P. J., et. al., contribution of Working Group II to the Fourth Assessment Report of the Intergovernmental Panel on Climate Change 2007 (2007).

[19] http://www.greenbookspecs.org/

[20] Opportunities for Interagency Collaboration and Coordination on Modeling for Coastal Inundation Hazard Reduction, National Science and Technology Council, Subcommittee on Disaster Reduction (2010).

[21] Sea Level Rise and Inundation Community Workshop, Ocean Research and Resources Advisory Panel of JSOST (2009).

[22] Final Recommendations of the Interagency Ocean Policy Task Force, White House Council on Environmental Quality, (2010).

[23] U.S. Department of Defense Quadrennial Defense Review Report, Department of Defense, (February, 2010)

[24] http://www.state.gov/documents/organization/140689.pdf

[25] Mitigation includes investments in clean energy and sustainable landscapes. Separate initiatives are being led by the Department of State and USAID to support low emissions

development strategies and reductions in emissions from deforestation and forest degradation (REDD+).

[26] See Appendix E for a more detailed summary of the five public outreach meetings.

[27] All public comments received on the interim progress report can be viewed at http://www.whitehouse.gov/administration/eop/ceq/initiatives/ adaptation/comments.

[28] See http://www.whitehouse.gov/administration/eop/ceq/initiatives/adaptation/publicmeetings for a complete agenda and archived webcast of all public outreach meetings.

In: Adapting to Climate Change   ISBN: 978-1- 61942-749-5
Editors: G. Robinson and L. K. Moore   © 2012 Nova Science Publishers, Inc

Chapter 2

FEDERAL ACTIONS FOR A CLIMATE RESILIENT NATION[*]

The White House Council on Environmental Quality

LIST OF ACRONYMS

BLM	Bureau of Land Management
CDC	Centers for Disease Control
CEQ	Council on Environmental Quality
CSC	Climate Science Centers
DOE	Department of Energy
DOI	Department of the Interior
DOT	Department of Transportation
EPA	Environmental Protection Agency
FEMA	Federal Emergency Management Agency
FTA	Federal Transit Administration
HUD	Department of Housing and Urban Development
LCC	Landscape Conservation Cooperatives
MCC	Millennium Challenge Corporation
NASA	National Aeronautics and Space Administration
NCA	National Climate Assessment
NFIP	National Flood Insurance Program

---

[*] This is an edited, reformatted and augmented version of a Progress Report of the Interagency Climate Change Adaptation Task Force dated October 28, 2011.

NOAA	National Oceanic and Atmospheric Administration
NOC	National Ocean Council
NPS	National Park Service
OSTP	Office of Science and Technology Policy
REA	Rapid Ecoregional Assessments
RISA	Regional Integrated Sciences and Assessments
RPA	Regional Plan Association
Task	Interagency Climate Change Adaptation Task Force
USACE	U.S. Army Corps of Engineers
USAID	U.S. Agency for International Development
USDA	U.S. Department of Agriculture
USFS	U.S. Forest Service
USFWS	U.S. Fish and Wildlife Service
USGCRP	U.S. Global Change Research Program
USGS	U.S. Geological Survey
WARN	Water/Wastewater Agency Response Network

EXECUTIVE SUMMARY

In October 2009, President Obama signed Executive Order 13514, *Federal Leadership in Environmental and Energy Performance*, which sets sustainability goals for federal agencies and focuses on making improvements in agency environmental, energy, and economic performance. The Executive Order charged the Interagency Climate Change Adaptation Task Force with providing recommendations on how federal policies, programs, and planning efforts can better prepare the United States for climate change. In October 2010, the task force recommended a set of policy goals and actions in its Progress Report to the president. The task force outlined how the Federal Government should work with local, state, and tribal partners to provide leadership, coordination, science, and services to address climate risks to the nation as well as federal assets and operations. In the 2010 Report, the task force committed to providing an update on federal government adaptation progress in 2011. This report provides that update in five key adaptation areas that align with the policy goals set forth by the task force in 2010:

Integrating Adaptation into Federal Government Planning and Activities: Agencies are taking steps to manage climate impacts to Federal agency missions, programs, and operations to ensure that resources are invested wisely and federal services remain effective for the American people. Agencies are developing climate adaptation plans to identify their vulnerabilities and prioritize activities that reduce climate risk.

Building Resilience to Climate Change in Communities: Recognizing that most adaptation occurs at the local level, federal agencies are working with diverse stakeholders in communities to prepare for a range of extreme weather and climate impacts (e.g. flooding, drought, and wildfire) that put people, property, local economies, and ecosystems at risk.

Improving Accessibility and Coordination of Science for Decision Making: To advance understanding and management of climate risks, the federal government is working to develop strong partnerships, enhance regional coordination of climate science and services, and provide accessible information and tools to help decision makers develop strategies to reduce extreme weather impacts and climate risks.

Developing Strategies to Safeguard Natural Resources in a Changing Climate: Recognizing that American communities depend on natural resources and the valuable ecosystem services they provide, agencies are working with key partners to create a coordinated set of national strategies to help safeguard the nation's valuable freshwater, ocean, fish, wildlife, and plant resources in a changing climate.

Enhancing Efforts to Lead and Support International Adaptation: To promote economic development, regional stability, and U.S. security interests around the world, the federal government is supporting a range of bilateral and multilateral climate change adaptation activities and coordinating defense, development and diplomacy policies to take into account growing climate risks.

Extreme weather and other climate change impacts pose significant social, economic, and environmental risks to the United States. The U.S. Government has a responsibility to reduce climate risks to public health and safety, economic well-being, natural resources, and federal programs and services. While much work remains, this report describes important federal progress toward the task force's strategic vision of a *resilient, healthy, and prosperous nation in the face of a changing climate.*

INTRODUCTION

The Interagency Climate Change Adaptation Task Force (hereafter task force) was established in 2009 to assess key steps needed to help the federal government understand and adapt to climate change. The task force is comprised of senior representatives from over 20 Departments and Agencies (Appendix A) and is co-chaired by the Council on Environmental Quality (CEQ), the Office of Science and Technology Policy (OSTP), and the National Oceanic and Atmospheric Administration (NOAA). As part of Executive Order 13514, President Obama directed the task force to examine how the federal government can better prepare the United States for climate impacts. In October 2010, the task force submitted a Progress Report to the president outlining a set of federal climate adaptation policy goals (Appendix B) and guiding principles (Appendix C). This report provides an update on Federal Government adaptation.

In the 2010 Progress Report, the task force called on federal agencies to demonstrate leadership on climate change adaptation. Rising sea levels, drought, extreme weather events, loss of land and sea ice, and other climate-related impacts threaten communities, ecosystems, and federal services and assets. As people in the United States and around the globe experience these impacts, the federal government will face growing demands for accurate climate information, disaster risk reduction, and preparedness and response support. Through stakeholder and public listening sessions, outreach events, and online comments, the 2010 Task Force Report determined that the Federal Government has a responsibility to safeguard federal services and resources and to help states, tribes, and communities manage climate- related risks by improving access to climate information, enhancing coordination and capacity, and leading and supporting actions that reduce vulnerability and increase resilience.

Federal agencies are taking steps to prepare the nation for the impacts of climate change and have demonstrated significant progress towards the task force's adaptation policy goals in five key areas. These efforts are informed by the guiding principles developed by the task force and ensure that federal resources are invested wisely and that the federal government's operations and services remain effective in a changing climate. Going forward, the task force will continue to support and coordinate these and other federal actions to realize the task force's vision of *a resilient, healthy, and prosperous nation in the face of a changing climate.*

KEY AREAS OF FEDERAL ADAPTATION PROGRESS

- Integrating Adaptation into Federal Government Planning Activities
- Building Resilience to Climate Change in Communities
- Improving Accessibility and Coordination of Science for Decision Making
- Developing Strategies to Safeguard Natural Resources in a Changing Climate
- Enhancing Efforts to Lead and Support International Adaptation

---

The task force has played an important leadership and coordination role in the federal government's adaptation activities. The task force directly supports federal adaptation efforts related to communities, public health, insurance, science and services, natural resources (e.g., freshwater, oceans, fish, wildlife and plants), international contexts, and non-federal partnerships and outreach. In addition, the task force provides a forum for interagency collaboration on adaptation and is consulted regularly by federal agencies and non-federal entities for adaptation expertise, coordination, and partnership opportunities.

The Need to Adapt

Climate change impacts pose significant social, economic, and environmental risks to the United States and the global community. As documented in the latest U.S. National Climate Assessment (NCA) report, *Global Climate Change Impacts in the United States,* and the National Research Council's report series on *America's Climate Choices,* communities across the nation are already experiencing a range of climatic changes, including more frequent and extreme precipitation events, longer wildfire seasons, reduced snowpack, extreme heat events, increasing ocean temperatures, and rising sea levels.[1,2] The impacts from these changes are affecting livelihoods, infrastructure, ecosystems, food production, energy supply, national security, and the cultural heritage of populations and communities. Certain communities and ecological systems are particularly vulnerable to these impacts. We know enough about climate risks to take actions now that ensure a safer, more resilient and prosperous future.

DEFINITIONS OF KEY TERMS

Adaptation: Adjustment in natural or human systems to a new or changing environment that exploits beneficial opportunities or moderates negative effects.

Resilience: A capability to anticipate, prepare for, respond to, and recover from significant multihazard threats with minimum damage to social well-being, the economy, and the environment.

Risk: A combination of the magnitude of the potential consequence(s) of climate change impact(s) and the likelihood that the consequence(s) will occur.

Vulnerability: The degree to which a system is susceptible to, or unable to cope with, adverse effects of climate change, including climate variability and extremes. Vulnerability is a function of the character, magnitude, and rate of climate variation to which a system is exposed, its sensitivity, and its adaptive capacity.

Source: National Research Council. 2011. *America's Choices Climate* : www.nap.edu/catalog.php?record_id=12781

Climate change is expected to significantly affect the United States. By the end of this century, global sea level is expected to rise by more than 2 feet in a low emissions scenario or nearly 3.5 feet in a higher emissions scenario.[3] Higher sea levels, especially in combination with storm surge, will increasingly inundate U.S. coastal communities and threaten coastal ecosystems and infrastructure, such as military installations.[4] Heat waves are expected to become more frequent and intense, posing a threat to human health and agriculture.[5] For rivers fed by snowpack, runoff will continue to occur earlier, with reduced flows late in the summer, and the potential for water shortages that can affect the supply of water for drinking, agriculture, electricity production, and ecosystems.[6] Economic, social, and natural systems are also inter-connected on a global scale, meaning that climate impacts in other regions of the world can pose serious economic and security risks to the United States. Increases in extreme weather and climate events will contribute to food and water scarcity, which can intensify existing tensions over access to life-sustaining resources.

Extreme weather and greater climate variability is expected to become more common in the future.[7] While it is not possible to attribute any individual extreme event to climate change, these events do provide valuable insight into the climate-related vulnerabilities and challenges faced by the United States. In April 2011, the United States experienced record-breaking floods, tornadoes, drought, and wildfires all within a single month. As of September 2011, NOAA's National Climatic Data Center had already reported ten weather events from 2011 for which damages and/or costs reached or exceeded $1 billion each,[8] exceeding the previous *annual* record of nine events recorded over the entire year in 2008. NOAA estimates the total damage of property and economic impacts for all weather-related disasters during the spring and summer of 2011 at more than $45 billion.[9] The severe and costly losses suffered during recent extreme weather events demonstrate the importance of increasing the resilience of the United States to climate variability and change in order to reduce economic damages and prevent loss of life.

The Obama Administration is committed to reducing the magnitude of future climate impacts by curbing greenhouse gas emissions and advancing a clean energy economy. However, a range of climate impacts are unavoidable. To manage these risks, we must identify key threats, prioritize activities that reduce our vulnerability, initiate actions that promote resilience, and enhance preparedness capabilities.[10]

> *"The City of Grand Rapids is addressing various climate-related threats such as extreme heat and more intense precipitation events. We see these climate strategies as an extension of responsible governance and an imperative investment in the future prosperity of our city. As an inland watershed city, we have focused on restoring and maintaining a high quality of water in the Grand River with over $240 million in combined sewer separation investment. This prepares us for ever-increasing precipitation levels now and into the future."*
> - George K. Heartwell Mayor, Grand Rapids, MI

Adaptation can involve a range of actions taken by individuals, businesses, and governments, such as: a farmer choosing to grow a different crop variety better suited to warmer or drier conditions; a company deciding to relocate key facilities away from coastal areas vulnerable to sea level rise and hurricanes; a community updating its ordinances to protect wetland habitat that provides critical ecosystem services like flood protection; a city developing early warning systems for severe storms; and a federal agency increasing its water- use efficiency at regional facilities to prepare for more frequent and severe drought. As demonstrated by these examples, there are management strategies at all levels of government and in all sectors that can help communities and businesses adapt to climate variability and change.

Local, State, and Private Sector Adaptation

Across the country, cities, towns, tribes, and states are leading efforts to reduce climate change risks. As of January 2011, eleven states had completed adaptation plans, four had plans in progress, and eight had recommended developing adaptation plans in their State Climate Action Plans.[11] Local adaptation efforts are emerging as well. The City of Chicago, for example, anticipating a hotter and wetter future, is already taking steps to adapt such as repaving alleyways with permeable materials to handle greater rainfall and reduce flood risks, and planting trees that can tolerate warmer conditions.[12]

> *"With the multiplier effect [of economic growth, subsidence, and climate change], the amount of economic loss to the Gulf Coast could rise to $700 billion, the gross domestic product for the entire region for one year. No region in the country can afford to lose their entire GDP once every 20 years... Doing nothing is not an acceptable plan. That's a plan to put Entergy out of business, a plan for misery and suffering for our customers and a plan that would devastate a region already economically impaired."*
>
> - J. Wayne Leonard
> Chairman and CEO, Entergy Corporation
> www.entergy.com/news_room/newsrelease.aspx?nr_id=1906

The private sector is also taking action to adapt to climate change. Investors are increasing pressure on firms, as evidenced by a record 101 shareholder resolutions in 2010 calling on North American companies to manage climate change risks.[13] Mounting losses from natural disasters are also shifting the business environment. In a 2011 global survey of businesses, nearly nine out of ten firms reported that they suffered climate impacts in the last three years.[14] Businesses are starting to take preventive action to protect their assets, employees, and operations from climate change risks. In the same survey, approximately 22 percent of North American firms reported actively making changes within their business to minimize climate risks and damages.

As highlighted throughout this report, the task force and its member agencies interact with business, local government, tribes, and other decision makers to learn from their successes and challenges and to understand what science and services they need to manage the impacts of climate change. Promoting and coordinating this dialogue will continue to be an essential element of the federal government's role moving forward.

Report Scope

This report provides a task force update on progress in five key areas at the core of federal efforts to advance a national climate adaptation strategy and build a climate resilient nation. These five areas closely align with the recommended policy goals in the 2010 Task Force Report (Appendix B) and also reflect how adaptation actions complement and intersect with one another. The examples of progress described in this report include technical assistance projects, regional partnerships, scientific advancements, and programs that foster adaptation. All of these efforts, with their diversity and breadth, demonstrate the federal government's progress toward the task force's 2010 policy goals.

INTEGRATING ADAPTATION INTO FEDERAL GOVERNMENT PLANNING AND ACTIVITIES

Highlights

- Federal agencies are beginning to more closely identify and manage climate-related risks and to implement actions that reduce climate change vulnerability and increase resilience of the nation.
- Federal agencies are developing agency-specific plans to strengthen existing adaptation efforts and establish long-term priorities to respond to the challenges and opportunities that climate change poses to their missions, operations, and programs.

Climate change will challenge the missions, operations, and programs of federal agencies. To ensure resilience and save taxpayer dollars in the long-run, the federal government has a responsibility to reduce climate risks as part of ongoing agency planning. federal agencies play a significant role in managing our nation's natural resources and infrastructure, including roads, airports, national parks, fisheries, dams, levees, and military installations. These natural and built assets are increasingly threatened in a changing climate, for example, by floods, droughts, hurricanes, and other disasters. federal agencies are partnering with tribes, states, and communities to better prepare for and manage these risks.

As directed by Executive Order 13514 and recommended by the task force, federal agencies are evaluating how climate variability and change are impacting their operations and services, and they are beginning to integrate adaptation into agency planning processes. Federal progress is evident from (1) newly established federal agency adaptation policies; (2) increased sharing of climate adaptation expertise and information across agencies; and (3) ongoing development of adaptation plans in accordance with the task force's guiding principles, including applying risk management methods and tools to their adaptation efforts. These adaptation plans will include assessments of how climate change may impact agency missions and operations, as well as identify necessary adjustments to reduce risk, avoid unnecessary costs, and take advantage of opportunities.

U.S. DEPARTMENT OF TRANSPORTATION ASSISTS MOBILE, ALABAMA WITH INFRASTRUCTURE PROTECTION

In 2003, the U.S. Department of Transportation (DOT) initiated the first part of the Gulf Coast Study, a comprehensive analysis of climate risks to transportation infrastructure in the Gulf Coast region and its communities. Phase 1 assessed transportation climate vulnerability in the Gulf Coast Region and was completed in 2008. Phase 2, conducted in cooperation with the South Alabama Regional Planning Commission, is focused on assessing potential climate change impacts and vulnerability of transportation in Mobile, Alabama. This effort will develop transferable tools that will help transportation planners assess the vulnerability of transportation systems to climate risks and determine how best to safeguard critical infrastructure. The study is expected to be completed in 2013.

Each adaptation plan will reflect the agency's core mission. For example, agencies with emergency management and health missions will likely focus on planning that reduces climate change risks to communities; those with infrastructure responsibilities will emphasize planning that enhances resilience and minimizes disruption; and agencies that support particular sectors (e.g. agriculture, energy) will focus on climate risks to production and security. The plans will help agencies integrate climate considerations into their existing planning and risk management processes.

SAN JUAN PUBLIC LANDS CENTER: FOREST SERVICE AND BUREAU OF LAND MANAGEMENT INTEGRATING CLIMATE SCIENCE INTO LAND MANAGEMENT

2002 Valley Fire that burned San Juan National Forest lands and many homes located at the urban interface (Credit: Craig Goodell, U.S. Forest Service)

The average temperature in the Southwest has increased roughly 1.5°F since the 1970s (USGCRP 2009: www.globalchange.gov/publications/reports). As a result, snowmelt is occurring earlier and more spring flooding and lower summer stream levels are projected for the future. Under the Service First initiative, the Bureau of Land Management's (BLM) San Juan Field Center and the U.S. Forest Service are working together at the San Juan Public Lands Center, which covers over 2.5 million acres in Southwestern Colorado. In the past year, the partners have developed a drought vulnerability model, a carbon storage map, an alpine monitoring program, and projections of future temperature and precipitation patterns. These tools and information will be used to adjust the timing of grazing allotments to ensure adequate vegetation and help land managers choose different tree species to plant that are more resilient to drought, fire, and pests.

Climate variability and change are already impacting federal programs and operations, as well as the citizens they serve. For example, the U.S. Forest Service (USFS) recognizes that climate change is a major challenge to its mission of sustaining the health, diversity, and productivity of the nation's forests and grasslands for present and future generations. Current climate change impacts, including changing temperatures and water flow patterns, can affect USFS-managed resources through increases in fire, drought, insect infestations, plant diseases, and invasive species. These impacts put at risk the many benefits Americans receive from forests, such as wood products, clean air, drinking water, and opportunities for recreation and tourism. The USFS National Roadmap for Responding to Climate Change identifies short- and long-term actions to reduce climate change risks to our nation's forests and grasslands. A scorecard tracks Roadmap implementation to ensure the agency is accountable for incorporating climate change considerations into existing programs.

Federal agencies have continued to make progress on the adaptation pilot projects outlined in the 2010 Task Force Report as well. The U.S. Army Corps of Engineers (USACE) is currently updating guidance on how the agency's projects, systems, and programs can respond to future changes in sea level.[15] In the long-term, USACE will use this information to incorporate climate change considerations into existing and new civil works infrastructure and ecosystem restoration projects in coastal areas to improve safety and resilience.

Federal agencies are at different stages of adaptation planning. Those with more experience are sharing lessons learned with their counterparts in other agencies. To respond to the 2010 task force's recommendations, federal agencies participated in a series of workshops during the summer of 2011 to share information and best practices for managing climate risks to public health, land and water resources, and infrastructure. Each agency is also adopting an internal policy to establish an adaptation planning goal and better understand the challenges and opportunities presented by a changing climate. Agencies have already begun initial actions to reduce climate impacts to their mission and operations, and they will develop and publish climate adaptation plans in the summer of 2012 to strengthen those efforts. This initial planning lays the foundation for agencies to more fully integrate actions into their operations and management to reduce climate risks to federal programs, services, and the nation.

BUILDING RESILIENCE TO CLIMATE CHANGE IN COMMUNITIES

Highlights

- Federal agencies are developing ways to incorporate climate adaptation into planning, emergency preparedness, and disaster recovery to protect communities and reduce losses.
- Federal agencies are providing data, information, and decision tools to reduce health and insurance risks related to climate impacts.

The 2010 Task Force Report recommended that the federal government help communities build resilience to climate change by integrating adaptation considerations into relevant federal programs, policies, and guidance. Across the United States, many communities are recognizing the social and economic importance of increasing resilience to climate-related impacts. A 2011 survey of 396 mayors from all 50 states found that over 30 percent are already taking climate impacts into account within their capital planning and improvement programs, demonstrating growing local concern about climate risks.[16] A climate-resilient community has the capability to anticipate, prepare for, and recover from climate impacts on public health and safety, the local economy, and natural resources. Planning for climate- related impacts is economically advantageous because it reduces the cost of disaster relief, improves infrastructure safety and reliability, and anticipates changes in ecosystems and the valuable services they provide.

The task force identified as a guiding principle in its 2010 Progress Report the need to prioritize the most vulnerable communities and create adaptation plans with meaningful involvement from all parts of society. Over the past year, the task force hosted workshops and listening sessions to solicit input from a wide variety of state, tribal, and local leaders on how the federal government can best support local adaptation efforts. Overwhelmingly, community stakeholders said they need reliable and accessible information to evaluate their vulnerabilities to climate change and to understand the costs and benefits of taking action to reduce local risks.

Through the task force and related interagency efforts, and in response to input from non-federal partners and stakeholders, the federal government is making progress in enhancing the ability of communities to promote resilience to climate impacts. This progress is evident from (1) use of existing federal resources, programs, and leadership to help communities reduce climate risks; (2) availability of information and decision support from federal agencies to protect public health, livelihoods, and well-being in a changing climate; and (3) initial steps to integrate climate change risks into insurance mechanisms. The actions discussed below are important steps toward meeting the 2010 Progress Report policy goal to address key cross-cutting issues related to climate change adaptation.

> *"In many smaller coastal towns that are going to be affected, the concern is not about expanding the current water and sewer infrastructure systems in a smart way. Rather, it is about moving infrastructure that has been in the ground for decades. Some of my pipes are over 100 years old. Smaller, low- wealth communities cannot possibly undertake the financial burden of system relocations without grants from the federal government."*
> - Brian A. Roth
> Mayor, Plymouth, NC on sea level rise

Working with Communities to Reduce Climate Risks

Communities and the federal government are now working in partnership to improve the ability of communities to prepare for climate change. For example, the U.S. Forest Service and the National Association of State Foresters co-sponsor Firewise Communities, a program that educates residents, planners, and community leaders about how to enhance safety and preparedness for wildfires.

Federal agencies are also developing ways to incorporate climate adaptation into emergency preparedness and disaster recovery to protect communities and reduce losses. The Federal Emergency Management Agency (FEMA) has found that every dollar spent by the agency on hazard mitigation provides the nation with about four dollars in future benefits.[17] FEMA, the U.S. Army Corps of Engineers (USACE), and state agencies are helping to address flood risks through the Silver Jackets program, which creates interagency teams to simplify access to critical flood risk mitigation and planning resources. It also provides communities with a single point of contact to the federal government on these issues. Additionally, the NOAA-led U.S. Integrated Ocean Observing System Program partners federal agencies with Regional Coastal Ocean Observing Systems across the country to provide coastal communities with more accurate estimates of the environmental effects of climate variability to inform community planning and reduce potential hazards.

NOAA AND PARTNERS SUPPORT DROUGHT PREPAREDNESS

The National Oceanic and Atmospheric Administration (NOAA), the National Integrated Drought Information System, National Drought Mitigation Center, and state partners created a Guide to Community Drought Preparedness, a free resource that helps communities with drought monitoring, communication, and education on drought mitigation and response. The guide has been used successfully in drought-prone communities that range in size from 7,000 residents (Nebraska City, NE) to larger urban areas including Decatur, IL (population: 75,000) and Norman, OK (population: 100,000). The guide provides valuable examples of how municipalities can reduce the economic impacts of future droughts by building community resilience.

www.drought.unl.edu/Planning/PlanningProcesses/DroughtReadyCommunities. aspx

Ensuring the health and safety of communities both before and after a disaster also depends on transportation and water infrastructure remaining safe and functional in the case of extreme events. As the intensity and frequency of severe storms increase in a changing climate, transportation and water infrastructure will need to be more resilient to climate impacts. To respond to this challenge, the Federal Transit Administration (FTA) provides public transportation officials across the country with information on transit use during emergency response and on how to build the resilience of public transportation assets and services to weather and climate risks. The Environmental Protection Agency's (EPA) Water/Wastewater Agency

Response Network (WARN) helps water utility managers respond to and recover from emergencies that affect water system integrity and can lead to health risks from sewer system failures.

People and businesses depend on secure and reliable energy supplies for social well-being and economic prosperity. More frequent and longer periods of drought anticipated with climate change will impact water supplies needed for energy production.[18] The Department of Energy (DOE) is working with the Western Governors' Association, the Western Electricity Coordinating Council, and the Electric Reliability Council of Texas on an energy-water initiative that supports electricity transmission planning in the western United States, taking into account reductions in water availability in a changing climate. The project will yield a comprehensive package of regional planning models and data that supplement interconnection-wide transmission planning studies with information on regional water availability and demand. These resources will help to shape climate resilient electricity generation options to meet the energy needs of a growing economy and population.

Federal agencies are also considering how existing grant programs can be used to encourage community adaptation. For example, the Department of Housing and Urban Development's (HUD) Sustainable Communities Regional Planning Grants encourage grant recipients to integrate climate adaptation into their regional housing, land use, and transportation planning. The Regional Plan Association (RPA) of New York City is one of a number of HUD grantees incorporating climate information to enhance resilience of critical infrastructure to severe storms and coastal flooding. The RPA will also assess urban design implications of flood protection standards to develop new example standards, codes, and regulations for municipalities that will better equip them to adapt to extreme climate conditions.

> *"Swinomish people are inheritors of the traditional knowledge of the Skagit territory...our people carry over 10,000 years of knowledge of our traditional area. We are experienced in the adaptation methods within our respected homelands and waters. So we urge you to invest in our knowledge. We have survived many challenges impacting the sustainability of our way of life, and we are still here, still adapting."*
>
> - Brian Cladoosby
> Chairman, Swinomish Tribe

While federal agencies have made progress in helping communities build resilience to climate change impacts, much more can be done, particularly for vulnerable populations. Within communities, some populations – such as children, elderly and low-income citizens–are more vulnerable to climate impacts due to higher sensitivity to health threats.[19] Tribal nations are also disproportionately affected by climate change because of their strong dependence on natural resources for economic development, subsistence, social cohesion, and culture.[20]

To help respond to these impacts on tribes, the Department of the Interior's (DOI) Bureau of Indian Affairs announced a competitive climate change tribal grant program in Fiscal Year 2011. These grants will enable tribal participation and representation in climate change-related activities occurring around the country. The funds will also help tribes develop and implement climate change projects and strategies to benefit tribal resources and communities. Partners will include the U.S. Forest Service (USFS), Bureau of Land Management (BLM), U.S. Fish and Wildlife Service (USFWS), National Park Service (NPS), and tribes. The federal government will continue to strengthen partnerships with communities and tribes to reduce climate change risks, particularly those that disproportionately affect vulnerable populations.

Protecting Public Health in a Changing Climate

Recognizing that climate variability and change pose health risks, the 2010 Task Force Report recommended that the federal government address climate change in public health activities. Climate change can heighten the risk of illnesses and injuries, exacerbate many existing health conditions, and change the patterns of where diseases are transmitted by insects and other vectors. Health is also affected by the safety and availability of food, water, indoor air quality, and energy, which may be compromised during and after extreme weather events. Extreme weather events, intense heat waves, and climate-induced degradation of air and water quality may overwhelm our already overburdened public health systems.[21] Protecting public health is an integral part of reducing the climate risks facing communities.

Federal agencies are making progress to address these challenges and promote healthy communities in the face of a changing climate. For example, the Center for Disease Control and Prevention (CDC) has launched the Climate-Ready States and Cities Initiative to help state and city health departments prepare for and monitor emerging health risks exacerbated by climate change. The CDC is currently connecting ten city and state health departments with climate scientists to understand potential impacts and identify health risks to their specific geographic area. Participating health departments are also developing strategies to determine the effects of climate change on human health and vulnerable populations.

Federally-provided tools are helping communities develop cost-effective ways to reduce health risks from climate impacts as well. The U.S. Forest Service provides decision-making tools that help communities plan tree plantings as low-cost ways of improving storm water management and flood control while reducing the urban "heat island" effect. By lowering air temperatures and increasing shade, the new trees improve quality of life.

FLOODING IMPACTS TO IOWA INFRASTRUCTURE

Flooding Impact on Bridge in Cedar Rapids, Iowa, July 2008 (Credit: Susie Shapira, FEMA)

Iowa has experienced catastrophic flooding three times in the past 17 years. The floods of 2008 rank in the top ten natural disasters in U.S. history and highlight the risks of Iowa's changing climate. The EPA and FEMA worked with stakeholders in Iowa in 2010 to coordinate hazard mitigation with current and future land-use decisions to increase community safety and help reduce economic losses from future flooding. EPA and FEMA are also coordinating to help other communities make cost-effective choices for housing and infrastructure systems that reduce climate risks to communities.

Integrating Climate Change Risks into Insurance Mechanisms

Insurance is one of several options available to individuals, businesses, and communities to manage risks posed by extreme weather and climate change. However, with continued development in areas exposed to flood hazards, especially in coastal areas, our nation's flood risk is increasing. In the 2010 Progress Report, the task force recommended facilitating the incorporation of climate change risks into insurance mechanisms. The federal government is assessing ways to develop more realistic risk-based pricing signals for public insurance and to raise public awareness of climate and extreme weather-related risks.

With task force leadership, a federal interagency group is exploring options for a public-private partnership to develop an open-source risk assessment model. This strategy aims to provide a consistent, accessible, no-cost resource for communities and insurance providers to assess risks from extreme weather events and climate change. The work on the risk assessment model will continue under the National Science and Technology Council's Subcommittee on Disaster Reduction.

Recent extreme events also highlight the need for a strong National Flood Insurance Program (NFIP: administered by FEMA), which enables homeowners in participating communities to purchase insurance protection against losses from flooding. In spring 2011, persistent rainfall combined with melting snowpack caused widespread flooding in some of the major rivers across the United States, including the Ohio, Mississippi, and Missouri.[22] FEMA is currently analyzing options to address concerns about the NFIP, including the inherent weaknesses caused by program subsidies and the cost of insurance, the methods by which flood risks are modeled and depicted on maps given expected changes in future hydrological conditions, and the low market penetration of flood insurance in floodplains.

FEMA is currently working with other federal agencies and academic experts to assess the impacts of climate change on the NFIP. Additionally, FEMA is undertaking a study on reforming the NFIP to reduce flood risks, improve flood risk communication, remove barriers for greater private sector participation in flood insurance, address affordability of insurance, and ensure fiscal soundness. FEMA will publish recommendations on these two issues in 2011.

IMPROVING ACCESSIBILITY AND COORDINATION OF SCIENCE FOR DECISION MAKING

Highlights
* The federal government is working to improve the accessibility and utility of climate information and tools to meet the needs of decision makers.
* The U.S. Global Change Research Program is advancing a process for timely climate research, assessments, and services to support adaptation planning across the country.

Decision makers need science that effectively informs and supports actions to enhance resilience to extreme events as well as climate variability and change.[23] The federal government plays an important role in ensuring that climate-related information and tools are accessible, timely, and relevant for decisions at multiple scales and in different contexts.

The federal government has made substantial progress towards the task force's 2010 policy goals of improving the integration of science into decision making and coordinating federal capabilities to support adaptation. Specifically, this progress is evident from (1) development of an interagency initiative to enhance coordination of regional climate science and services; (2) substantial strengthening of the National Climate Assessment; and (3) emergence of coordinating bodies and programs for addressing critical information needs and improving the utility and accessibility of federal science in support of adaptation. All of these efforts align with the task force's guiding principles that adaptation requires strong partnerships and should be grounded in the best-available science.

With task force leadership, federal agencies are undertaking efforts to enhance regional coordination of climate science and services. Under this initiative, partnerships between federal and non-federal climate-related programs will expand and strengthen in eight regions that cover the entire United States. These collaborations will support efficient and effective delivery of climate science, tools, services, and assessments to meet stakeholder needs and support adaptation planning within each region, integrating and leveraging the existing coordination efforts described below.

A number of federal efforts are already underway to strengthen regional partnerships on climate science and services. For example, DOI has initiated a landscape-level, science-based approach to informing management of natural resources through the development of a nationwide network of Climate Science Centers (CSC) and Landscape Conservation Cooperatives (LCC). DOI works in close partnership with NOAA's Regional Integrated Sciences and Assessments (RISA) teams to maximize cost-effectiveness while enhancing the federal government's collective ability to develop and provide critical science to a diverse array of stakeholders. CSCs will provide fundamental scientific information, tools, and techniques for land, water, wildlife, and cultural resource managers to anticipate, monitor, and adapt to climate change impacts. RISAs will contribute information and advance understanding within the regions by performing interdisciplinary research that addresses the diverse needs of decision makers, such as local farm and ranch organizations and emergency planners.

PREPAREDNESS FOR EXCESSIVE HEAT EVENTS

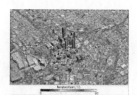

Thermal Photo of Atlanta, GA (Credit: NASA)

Climate change is expected to exacerbate threats to health by increasing the frequency, intensity, and duration of excessive heat events. However, most adverse health outcomes are preventable. Federal agencies are working with state and local officials to develop preparedness plans and tools that local emergency planners and decision makers can use to prepare for and respond to heat waves.

An Excessive Heat Event Guidebook developed by EPA, NOAA, DHS, and CDC helps community officials, emergency managers, and scientists develop city-specific heat response plans and early-warning systems. NASA and CDC are also working with Indiana University on pilot projects with Philadelphia, PA, Dayton, OH, and Phoenix, AZ to improve their heat watch/warning systems by integrating satellite measurements with social and health data to improve preparedness.

The National Climate Assessment (NCA), an interagency effort within the U.S. Global Change Research Program (USGCRP), is another core element of the federal government's effort to advance climate science and services. As mandated by the Global Change Research Act of 1990, the 2013 NCA synthesis report will include an evaluation of federal climate science activities and an assessment of current and future climate impacts on critical sectors (e.g. water, agriculture, energy, etc.). The newly redesigned NCA process is working to expand engagement of partners from every sector and region of the United States. Moving forward, the NCA is exploring options for increasing the accessibility and utility of its products through web-based deployment and other forms of communications. The NCA is also working to establish sustained capacity to deliver consistent and accurate impact, vulnerability, and risk information in support of adaptation decision- making. In addition, the NCA is working with federal agencies and other partners to develop physical, ecological, and societal indicators for tracking U.S. climate change impacts and vulnerabilities through time.

SCIENCE IN SUPPORT OF FIRE RESPONSE

Satellite Image of Texas Fires (Credit: NASA)

Federal agencies are providing scientific information and tools to help decision makers prepare for, respond to, and reduce the threat of fire to minimize fire-related loss of life and damages.

With seasonal forecasting, NOAA scientists warned Texas fire managers in December 2010 of impending extreme drought conditions that would lead to high fire risk. This long-range forecast helped decision makers pre-position local fire-fighting assets so that when the fire season arrived, first responders could act quickly to save lives and property.

When the burning escalated in spring 2011, as predicted, NOAA deployed specially trained National Weather Service (NWS) meteorologists to support forecasts that helped first responders battle the fires. The 13 NWS forecast offices serving Texas also provided drought information, high wind warnings, and short- and long-term weather forecasts.

Throughout the 2011 fire season, the U.S. Forest Service and DOI used science-based tools to provide information about expected fire behavior, risks of damage, and assistance needs.

ADDRESSING CLIMATE RISKS IN SOUTHEAST FLORIDA

Inundation (right) from a high tide in Fort Lauderdale, Florida (Credit: Broward County)

Southeast Florida is already experiencing the impacts of extreme weather and sea level rise, compromising drainage systems and sea walls during high tide events. With continued sea level rise and the prospect of more intense hurricanes and heavy downpours, the region faces greater risks of flooding, safe water supply shortages, infrastructure damage, and natural resource degradation. In response, Broward, Miami-Dade, Palm Beach, and Monroe Counties entered into the Southeast Florida Regional Climate Change Compact in 2010 to address these threats collaboratively. The South Florida Water Management District and Climate Leadership Initiative have been prominent partners in this effort.

Local and regional offices of federal agencies—including USACE, NOAA, USGS, and EPA—have supported these counties with regional adaptation planning. For example, USACE and NOAA provided technical assistance to evaluate threats of future sea level rise. USGS applied advanced hydrologic models and provided financial resources to support projects related to saltwater intrusion of groundwater supplies and flood risks. EPA provided coordination support, helping connect the Compact partners with critical technical, planning, and programmatic resources.

Last year, the federal government launched another major effort to address critical adaptation information needs of practitioners and managers. An interagency Adaptation Science Workgroup, initiated by the task force and transitioned to the USGCRP in 2010, is coordinating science in support of adaptation across federal agencies, identifying ways to improve the deployment of adaptation-relevant science, providing scientific support for agencies as they implement adaptation plans required under EO 13514, and developing metrics and guidance that practitioners can use to evaluate the success of their adaptation efforts.

Many other federal efforts are also underway to provide decision-relevant climate information in easily understood and useful formats. The Extension Disaster Education Network,[24] a multi-state Extension Services effort supported by U.S. Department of Agriculture's (USDA) National Institute of Food and Agriculture and NOAA Sea Grant, provides county educators with science-based tools and information to help communities prepare for, respond to, and recover from natural and manmade disasters. The USGS's LandSat program provides satellite imagery online[25] that helps land owners and managers observe and better manage forests and agricultural lands. NOAA also recently updated its U.S. Climate Normals data online.[26] Access to this information helps farmers make planting decisions and electricity utility managers set appropriate rates. Through the Prediction of Worldwide Energy Resource (POWER) project and web portal,[27] NASA provides user-friendly weather and solar data that help the energy, building, and agricultural industries plan for climate impacts. The USGCRP is also exploring options for developing and maintaining an online interagency global change information portal/system to provide "one-stop shopping" for climate-related information.

> *"The Harris County Flood Control District and many other local and state flood risk reduction agencies look to the federal government for unified, targeted climate change research to establish public policy and guidance based on best-available scientific research. We encourage the inclusion of local and state officials in the research, policy, and guidance development since all of the impact and much of the cost of any decision to incorporate, or not incorporate, climate change as a design factor will be borne by local and state entities."*
>
> - Steve Fitzgerald
> Chief Engineer
> Harris County Flood Control District, Texas

A great deal of work is still required to provide accessible information that meets the diverse set of adaptation planning, implementation, and evaluation challenges faced by communities and practitioners. Building upon and strengthening partnerships between federal and non-federal entities will be key to advancing adaptation efforts across the country. Developments in information, tools, and services, particularly at local-to-regional scales, will be needed to better support planning needs. These challenges also create opportunities and incentives to improve coordination among federal agencies, leverage existing and future efforts, and develop the innovative partnerships required to integrate climate information into public and private planning, evaluation, and investment.

DEVELOPING STRATEGIES TO SAFEGUARD NATURAL RESOURCES IN A CHANGING CLIMATE

Highlights

- The federal government worked with stakeholders to develop a *National Action Plan* for managing freshwater resources in a changing climate in order to assure adequate water supplies and protect water quality, human health, property, and aquatic ecosystems.
- Federal agencies are partnering with state, tribal and local representatives to develop strategies for safeguarding our nation's oceans, fish, wildlife, and plants.

Over the coming decades, the valuable natural resources and ecosystem services on which people depend will be increasingly affected by warming temperatures, rising seas, and more frequent and severe drought, among other expected climatic changes. In some cases, major, rapid disruptions to ecosystems may occur when ecological thresholds are crossed due to climate change in combination with other stressors.[28] The federal government has made significant progress in developing strategies to safeguard natural resources as recommended under the task force's policy goal to address key cross-cutting issues. This progress is evident from (1) completion of a *National Action Plan* to strengthen climate change adaptation for freshwater resources; (2) development of a strategic action plan to strengthen the resilience of coastal, ocean and Great Lakes communities and ecosystems to climate change; and (3) design of a strategy to reduce climate change impacts on the nation's fish, wildlife and plant resources and their habitats. The task force and the Council on Environmental Quality (CEQ) are regularly convening the groups charged with the development of these strategies to foster collaboration and to ensure that the plans are complementary.

> *"The Trinity River COMMON VISION Program has been a vanguard for effective floodplain management in North Central Texas... but our continued partnership with federal agencies like the U.S. Army Corps of Engineers and FEMA with our local governments is the key ingredient to our ongoing progress and accomplishment. Our agency, on behalf of our member local governments, remains committed to partnership to meet the public safety, environmental stewardship and overall quality of life needs of our region. We hope our federal partners are equally as committed in this effort to deal with the significant challenges of climate resilience in watershed and floodplain management."*
>
> - John Promise
> Director of Environment & Development North Central Texas Council of Governments

Managing Water Resources in a Changing Climate

Climate impacts pose significant challenges for water resource managers. These challenges include ensuring adequate groundwater and surface water supply for human consumption, ecological integrity, agriculture, industry, and energy as hydrologic conditions shift and drought becomes more prevalent. New problems may also arise for water managers working to protect human health and property, such as increased water- and vector-borne disease, increased difficulty in treating drinking water, and disruptions of power, water, sewer, and emergency services as a result of more extreme rainfall events. Changing water resource conditions will also create challenges for protecting the availability and quality of freshwater resources, habitat, and aquatic life.

Federal agencies have made substantial progress in improving water resource management in a changing climate. Member agencies of the task force developed a *National Action Plan: Priorities for Managing Freshwater Resources in a Changing Climate*. The *Plan* includes a national goal and six recommendations to help freshwater resource managers understand and reduce the risks of climate change to our nation's freshwater resources. It is designed to help freshwater resource managers assure adequate water supplies, safeguard water quality, and protect human life, health, and property. Key recommendations call for strengthening federal water data systems, building tools to help water facilities assess vulnerability to climate change, expanding water use efficiency, and supporting training and outreach to build climate change response capability in the water sector.

The *Plan* will be a foundation for federal agency efforts to manage water resources as the climate changes. In a related effort, the Department of Interior (DOI) delivered a report to Congress on how to strengthen data and information systems to better understand climate impacts on water.[29] DOI also produced a report on the risks and impacts to water supplies and management in the eight major river basins in the western United States.[30]

NEW YORK CITY PILOT FOR CLIMATE RESILIENCE EVALUATION AND AWARENESS TOOL

Treated sewage backed-up at Bronx Water Pollution Control Plant (Credit: NYC DEP)

In 2009, EPA worked with the New York City Department of Environmental Protection (DEP) to pilot the Climate Resilience Evaluation and Awareness Tool (CREAT). CREAT is a software tool designed to assist drinking water and wastewater utility owners and operators in understanding potential climate change threats to their utilities. CREAT allows users to assess adaptation options to address climate-related impacts using both traditional risk assessment and scenario-based decision making. The DEP is now using the tool to complement a comprehensive study to develop an adaptation strategy to address increasing population demand for water services and minimize impacts of heavy rain and storm surge to New York City's drainage and wastewater management systems.

water.epa.gov/infrastructure/watersecurity/climate/creat.cfm

In addition, the federal government has made important progress toward improving water-use efficiency to reduce climate change impacts. For example, DOI's WaterSMART program continues to provide support to help states deal with rapid population growth, climate change, aging infrastructure, and land use changes. As part of that effort, DOI awarded *$24 million in funding for new water conservation and energy efficiency projects* in Western states, saving enough water annually to serve a population of 400,000. Many of the WaterSMART projects involve relatively inexpensive improvements and conventional technology. An irrigation company in Washington State, for instance, will simply replace open ditches with pipes. By preventing seepage loss and reducing pumped water demands, the project will save approximately 2.5 billion gallons of water and 4.3 million kWh of electricity per year. EPA's WaterSense program also provides tools to decrease indoor and outdoor residential water use through more efficient products and practices. In 2010, WaterSense helped consumers save more than 79 billion gallons of water, $1.3 billion in water and sewer bills, and 10.8 billion kWh of electricity.

In the agricultural sector, the USDA is working with farmers in the Environmental Quality Incentives Program (EQIP) to improve water-use efficiency through measures that allow farmers to grow more crops with less water. In 2010, 28 projects totaling more than $60 million supported water conservation efforts in nine states. In Colorado, for example, technology funded under EQIP helps farmers monitor water-use data in real-time. This information helps them decide how much water to use on their crops, when to apply irrigation water, and what types of irrigation equipment to use.

Federal agencies are also working with communities to address challenges associated with managing water in a changing climate. NOAA's Lake Champlain Sea Grant program has educated local businesses and community leaders, residents, and students about how climate change can affect their communities. Climate models project an increase in heavy rainfall events in the Lake Champlain basin within the next century, leading to an increase in surface runoff, stream channel instability, flooding, pollutant loading, and altered aquatic ecosystems. Sea Grant has partnered with churches, small businesses, and medical parks to implement stormwater management best practices at three demonstration projects in Vermont.

Enhancing Resilience and Adaptation of the Nation's Coasts, Oceans, and Great Lakes to Climate Change and Ocean Acidification

Climate-related impacts pose serious threats to coastal communities and coastal, ocean and Great Lakes ecosystems. Coastal communities are projected to face significant risks of inundation from the combined impacts of sea level rise and storm surge from increased intensity of extreme events. The distribution and productivity of fish, invertebrate, and plant species are shifting in response to warming ocean waters.[31] Climate change is expected to lower the water levels of the Great Lakes, thereby altering habitat, water cycles and supply, and related economic activities. Ocean acidification is expected to have significant and largely negative impacts on marine biological diversity.[32]

In July 2010, President Obama signed Executive Order 13547, which established the nation's first-ever National Policy for Stewardship of the Ocean, our Coasts, and the Great Lakes, as well as an interagency National Ocean Council (NOC) to advance the Policy. The NOC is co-chaired by CEQ and OSTP, and includes representatives from 26 federal agencies. The NOC is currently developing a *Strategic Action Plan for Resiliency and Adaptation to Climate Change and Ocean Acidification*. The draft *Plan* proposes a coordinated approach to conducting research, observations, modeling, vulnerability assessments, and to providing information and guidance to support adaptation efforts. These advances will help communities and ecosystem stewards manage risks related to climate change and ocean acidification.

The federal government is working with partners to make progress toward improving the resilience of coastal communities and ecosystems to climate change risks. For instance, NOAA provides funds and technical assistance to support coastal states and communities to improve their resilience to climate change and coastal hazards. NOAA also supports Maryland's Coast-Smart Communities Initiative, which provides local decision makers with information and resources to plan for and adapt to sea level rise and coastal hazards. As a result of this effort, a number of Maryland communities have recently amended their building codes to require elevation buffers (i.e. freeboard) ranging from 1.5 to 2 feet for new and re-development projects to account for future sea level rise and more frequent flooding and inundation.

In coastal ecosystems across the country, federal agencies are supporting adaptation efforts. EPA's Climate Ready Estuaries program (CRE), for instance, has supported more than 30 coastal adaptation projects in collaboration with 19 National Estuary Programs from Charlotte Harbor, Florida to Puget Sound, Washington.[33] These projects have used the best-available science for the development of climate change vulnerability assessments and have developed ecosystem-based adaptation strategies. As another example, the U.S. Geological Survey (USGS) is mapping the distribution of key species in the low-lying islands and atolls of the

Papahanaumokuakea Marine National Monument in the Pacific, identifying those most vulnerable to sea level rise.

RESTORING TIDAL PROCESSES TO NISQUALLY ESTUARY IN WASHINGTON STATE

After a century of blocking tidal flow, the Brown Farm Dike was removed to inundate 762 acres of Nisqually National Wildlife Refuge in Washington State in October 2009. Along with 140 acres of tidal wetlands restored by the Nisqually Indian Tribe, this represents the largest tidal marsh restoration project in the Pacific Northwest to assist in recovery of Puget Sound salmon and wildlife populations. During the past decade, the refuge and partners have restored more than 22 miles of tidal slough systems and re-connected historic floodplains to the Puget Sound, enabling an increase of up to 50 percent in salt marsh habitat in this part of the Sound.

Partners have initiated restoration of more than 70 acres of riparian surge plain forest, an extremely depleted type of tidal forest important for juvenile salmon and songbirds. Restoration of the estuary is an adaptation approach that helps promote system resilience to climate change effects such as increased winter storms, loss of forest cover due to increases in insect infestations and fire, and sea level rise resulting in loss of shoreline.

Safeguarding Our Nation's Fish, Wildlife and Plants

Ecosystems are already significantly impacted by climate change. These impacts include large-scale shifts in species ranges and more fires, insect pests, disease pathogens, invasive species, and habitat loss.[34] Species respond differently to changes in climate, leading to alterations in community composition and mismatches in life history events (e.g. migration and blooming).[35] Climate change is likely to exacerbate existing stresses (e.g. habitat fragmentation and pollution) and negatively impact communities that rely on natural resources for their livelihood and economic prosperity. Some of these impacts will be irreversible, such as species extinctions and loss of coastal land as sea levels rise.

With state and tribal partners, the federal government has made significant progress toward developing a *National Fish, Wildlife, and Plants Climate Adaptation Strategy.*[36] Congress called for this *Strategy* in 2010, and it was endorsed by the task force in its 2010 Progress Report. The U.S. Fish and Wildlife Service (USFWS), NOAA, CEQ, and state wildlife agencies are co-leading the development of the Strategy using the best-available science and applying ecosystem-based approaches, in line with task force guiding principles. A draft *Strategy* is scheduled for public release in late 2011 and a final draft will be published by summer 2012.

While this *Strategy* takes shape, the federal government is taking actions to manage climate- related risks to natural resources. For instance, a collaborative group of federal agencies and no-ngovernmental organizations developed guidance for natural resource managers and other decision makers on climate change vulnerability assessments.[37] In addition, the USGS initiated a study to examine climate change influences on the survival of native trout and salmon across 11 Western states. The results of this study will support managers and stakeholders in developing appropriate adaptation strategies.

In the Sierra Nevada, California, the National Park Service (NPS) is leading a collaborative effort with the U.S. Forest Service and the USGS to analyze the vulnerability of ecosystems to changes in fire associated with climate change. Also, the Bureau of Land Management (BLM) is currently conducting ten Rapid Ecoregional Assessments (REAs) across the Western U.S and Alaska to promote cross-boundary collaboration and informed decision-making through the rapid synthesis of scientific data, identification of resource locations, and description of ecological status on a broad scale. These efforts facilitate collaborative development and prioritization of regional conservation, restoration, and climate adaptation strategies and actions.

SEA LEVEL RISE AND CONSERVATION STRATEGIES FOR THE PIPING PLOVER

Current and near-term decisions regarding coastal stabilization will strongly influence the effects of sea level rise on the Atlantic Coast Piping Plover, a threatened beach-nesting bird.

(Credit: G. Nieminen, U.S. Fish and Wildlife Service)

The U.S. Fish and Wildlife Service, U.S. Geological Survey, and National Park Service are collaborating with Virginia Tech University, state wildlife agencies, and non-governmental organizations to assess the effects of accelerating sea level rise on piping plover habitat. The effort uses cutting-edge models to develop piping plover habitat conservation recommendations that can be implemented by land managers and inform regulatory authorities. Collaborators anticipate that the model results may be readily translated to inform habitat management for other beach-dwelling species around the country.

ENHANCING EFFORTS TO LEAD AND SUPPORT INTERNATIONAL ADAPTATION

Highlights

- The federal government is working to identify and address the impacts of climate change that exacerbate conflict and social, economic, and political instability abroad.
- Select federal agencies have dedicated resources to support and build the capacity of partner countries and communities as they craft and implement climate-resilient development strategies.

In addition to domestic impacts, climate change exacerbates threats to communities, human development, and regional stability internationally. The impacts of climate change and extreme weather abroad can have serious economic and security implications for the United States. Conversely, actions that help countries reduce climate risks benefit broader U.S. development and foreign policy objectives.

The federal government has made progress toward the task force's policy goal of enhancing efforts to lead and support international adaptation. This progress is evident from (1) the development of a government-wide strategy to support multilateral and bilateral adaptation activities and to integrate adaptation into relevant U.S. foreign assistance programs; (2) delivery of targeted adaptation finance to support activities that reduce the risks of climate change and extreme weather through multilateral and bilateral channels; (3) design and implementation of complementary development, diplomacy and defense policies and actions that form an integrated approach to climate adaptation; and (4) outcomes from engagement in international climate negotiations and the global Adaptation Partnership.

In September 2010, President Obama issued the Presidential Policy Directive on Global Development (PPD). The PPD calls for the elevation of development as a core pillar of American foreign policy and addressing global climate change as a key development initiative. Adaptation to climate change is a central component and one of three important pillars of the PPD's Global Climate Change Initiative.

As part of the Global Climate Change Initiative, the federal government seeks to empower vulnerable developing countries and communities to strengthen their climate resilience, and therefore, their prospects for development and economic growth. Toward this goal, the Department of State, U.S. Agency for International Development (USAID), and the Department of the Treasury have dedicated resources to programs that support and build the capacity of partner countries and communities as they craft and implement climate-resilient development strategies. Other federal agencies, such as the Millennium Challenge Corporation (MCC) and the Overseas Private Investment Corporation, are also ensuring that their programs take climate change into consideration as appropriate.

The federal government is also working to reduce the potential impact of climate change on fragile or vulnerable countries to enhance stability and security. The National Security Staff convened technical, international development, intelligence, and defense agencies to coordinate actions to address international climate change impacts and strengthen their shared understanding of climate change risks to development, diplomacy, and defense. The Chairman of the Joint Chiefs of Staff, Admiral Mullen, released an updated National Military Strategy in 2010. The Strategy notes climate change in its description of the future security environment, and discusses conflict prevention in detail, emphasizing the savings associated with preventive action. With this strategic guidance, combatant commanders are able to consider climate risks in their theater campaign plans and undertake environmental cooperation with foreign militaries.

In 2010, the United States joined the rest of the world in taking an important step in meeting the climate and clean energy challenge at the United Nations Framework Convention on Climate Change Conference. All major economies agreed to take actions to reduce their emissions in a transparent way, which is key to limiting the magnitude of future climate change. Significant progress on how to address adaptation, finance, and technology transfer will help reduce climate change risks.

The United States is also engaging with global development partners and the private sector to promote knowledge sharing and coordinate adaptation investments. In 2010, the United States joined Costa Rica and Spain in chairing the global Adaptation Partnership. More than 20 developing and developed countries have participated in the Partnership to identify common adaptation priorities and improve coordination to scale up actions and financing. The State Department, USAID, NOAA, and EPA are collaborating to provide U.S. leadership to the Partnership by delivering workshops that address key adaptation challenges and by supporting communities of adaptation practitioners.

Woman gathering low-quality water from an open well in Matameye, Niger (Credit: John Furlow, USAID)

EXAMPLES OF PROGRESS TO REDUCE INTERNATIONAL CLIMATE RISKS

Pastoruri Glacier, Peru (Credit: John Furlow, USAID)

- The United States is helping countries prepare for potentially severe climate change impacts to water security. For example, glacier retreat could have a devastating impact on water supply in Andean nations, India, Nepal, Bangladesh, Afghanistan, Pakistan, and Central Asia. The United States is building capacity for water resource management and supporting research on hydrological cycles, glacier dynamics, and adaption for downstream communities.

- The United States is building climate resilience in Least Developed Countries (LDCs) that are most vulnerable to extreme weather and climate impacts. Support to the multilateral Pilot Program for Climate Resilience has leveraged $285 million in contributions from other developed country governments to help vulnerable developing countries, including several LDCs, pilot and demonstrate approaches for incorporating climate risk and resilience into development policies and planning.

- NASA and USAID's SERVIR program combines satellite and ground-based observations with models, providing environmental information that supports adaptation in developing countries in Central America and the Caribbean, East Africa, and the Hindu-Kush Himalayan region of South Asia.

- The United States is negotiating an updated Great Lakes Water Quality Agreement with Canada that will address climate change impacts.

Going forward, the U.S. Government will continue to help developing country partners assess and manage climate change risks. The U.S. Government will integrate climate adaptation across its development assistance portfolio, making investments more cost-effective and robust. The federal government is also committed to bringing its full capacities—including technical assistance, science, and technology—to support climate-resilient development programming around the world.

CONCLUSION

Preparing for climate change will enhance the safety, well-being, and livelihoods of American citizens and minimize disruption of the services on which they depend. With leadership and coordination from the task force, federal agencies are making important progress on identifying and managing risks associated with climate change. In particular, significant interagency efforts are underway to make information on climate impacts more accessible and useful to communities and decision makers across the country, effectively manage natural resources and critical U.S. infrastructure, and enhance efforts to promote adaptation internationally.

Over the next several years, the task force's efforts to reduce the nation's vulnerability to climate change will focus on enhancing regional coordination, strengthening and leveraging non-federal partnerships, and implementing federal agency adaptation planning. The task force will provide an update on federal adaptation progress in March 2014, following the release of the 2013 National Climate Assessment Synthesis Report.

Partnerships and actions across all scales will be necessary to more fully realize the task force's vision of *a resilient, healthy, and prosperous nation in a changing climate*. Agencies across the federal government are developing a diversity of non-federal partnerships to maximize opportunities for coordination and collaboration, and to exchange information and lessons learned with cities, states, tribes, and other nations that are incorporating adaptation into their own decision processes. The task force will work to align federal efforts with those of communities, states, tribes, and regions to reduce the risks of extreme events and climate impacts through adaptation. These collective efforts will help advance the nation toward a more sustainable future.

APPENDIX A. INTERAGENCY CLIMATE CHANGE ADAPTATION TASK FORCE MEMBERSHIP

Co-chair Agencies
Council on Environmental Quality
National Oceanic and Atmospheric Administration
Office of Science and Technology Policy

Member Departments and Agencies
Agency for International Development
Army Corps of Engineers
Council of Economic Advisors
Department of Agriculture
Department of Commerce
Department of Defense
Department of Education
Department of Energy
Department of Health and Human Services
Department of Homeland Security
Department of Housing and Urban Development
Department of the Interior
Department of State
Department of Transportation
Department of the Treasury
Environmental Protection Agency
Millennium Challenge Corporation
National Aeronautics and Space Administration
National Intelligence Council
National Economic Council
National Security Staff
Office of Management and Budget

APPENDIX B. 2011 PROGRESS REPORT STRUCTURE

The 2011 report discusses progress towards the task force's 2010 policy goals in a way that recognizes their synergies and interconnectedness. As the table outlines below, progress toward the 2010 cross-cutting goals related to community resilience, human health, and insurance is described in the *Building Resilience to Climate Change in Communities* section of the 2011 report, given the local relevance and benefits of these efforts. Progress toward the complementary goals of integrating science into decision-making and coordinating capabilities of the federal government are discussed together in the 2011 report section on *Improving Accessibility and Coordination of Science*. Finally, progress on freshwater, oceans, fish, wildlife, and plants adaptation efforts are discussed in the 2011 report section on *Strategies to Safeguard Natural Resources*, as these efforts represent components of national strategic action planning related to natural resources.

2011 PROGRESS REPORT STRUCTURE (IN BOLD)
2010 Policy Goals and Cross-Cutting Issues (in Italics)

Integrating Adaptation into Federal Government Planning and Activities

- *Encourage and Mainstream Adaptation Planning across the federal government*

Building Resilience to Climate Change in Communities

- *Cross-cutting issue: Build resilience to climate change in communities*
- *Cross-cutting issue: Protect human health by addressing climate change in public health activities*
- *Cross-cutting issue: Facilitate incorporation of climate change risks into insurance mechanisms*

Improving Accessibility and Coordination of Science for Decision Making

- *Improve Integration of Science into Decision Making*
- *Coordinate Capabilities of the federal government to Support Adaptation*

Developing Strategies to Safeguard Natural Resources in a Changing Climate

- *Cross-cutting issue: Improve water resource management in a changing climate*

- *Cross-cutting issue: Develop a strategic action plan focused on strengthening the resilience of coastal, ocean, and Great Lakes communities and ecosystems to climate change*
- *Cross-cutting issue: Develop a strategy for reducing the impacts of climate change on the nation's fish, wildlife, and plant resources and their habitats*

Enhancing Efforts to Lead and Support International Adaptation
- *Enhance Efforts to Lead and Support International Adaptation*

APPENDIX C. INTERAGENCY CLIMATE CHANGE ADAPTATION TASK FORCE GUIDING PRINCIPLES

GUIDING PRINCIPLES FOR ADAPTATION

Adopt Integrated Approaches: Adaptation should be incorporated into core policies, planning, practices, and programs whenever possible.

Prioritize the Most Vulnerable: Adaptation plans should prioritize helping people, places and infrastructure that are most vulnerable to climate impacts and be designed and implemented with meaningful involvement from all parts of society.

Use Best-Available Science: Adaptation should be grounded in the best-available scientific understanding of climate change risks, impacts, and vulnerabilities.

Build Strong Partnerships: Adaptation requires coordination across multiple sectors and scales and should build on the existing efforts and knowledge of a wide range of public and private stakeholders.

Apply Risk-Management Methods and Tools: Adaptation planning should incorporate risk management methods and tools to help identify, assess, and prioritize options to reduce vulnerability to potential environmental, social, and economic implications of climate change.

Apply Ecosystem-based Approaches: Adaptation should, where relevant, take into account strategies to increase ecosystem resilience and protect critical ecosystem services on which humans depend to reduce vulnerability of human and natural systems to climate change.

Maximize Mutual Benefits: Adaptation should, where possible, use strategies that complement or directly support other related climate or environmental initiatives, such as efforts to improve disaster preparedness, promote sustainable resource management, and reduce greenhouse gas emissions including the development of cost-effective technologies.

Continuously Evaluate Performance: Adaptation plans should include measureable goals and performance metrics to continuously assess whether adaptive actions are achieving desired outcomes.

End Notes

[1] USGCRP. (2009). *Global Climate Change Impacts in the United States.* www.global change.gov/publications/reports

[2] National Research Council. (2011). *America's Climate Choices.* The National Academies Press. Washington, DC www.nap.edu/catalog.php?record_id=12781

[3] USGCRP. (2009). *Global Climate Change Impacts in the United States.* www.globalchange. gov/publications/reports

[4] US Department of Defense. (2010). *Quadrennial Defense* Review. www.defense.gov/qdr/

[5] USGCRP. (2009). *Global Climate Change Impacts in the United States.* www.globalchange. gov/publications/reports

[6] USGCRP. (2009). *Global Climate Change Impacts in the United States.* www.globalchange. gov/publications/reports

[7] USGCRP. (2009). *Global Climate Change Impacts in the United States.* www.globalchange. gov/publications/reports

[8] NOAA. (2011). *Billion Dollar US Weather Disasters.* National Climatic Data Center. www. ncdc.noaa.gov/oa/reports/billionz.html

[9] NOAA. (2011). *Billion Dollar US Weather Disasters.* National Climatic Data Center. www.ncdc.noaa.gov/oa/reports/billionz.html

[10] National Research Council. (2011). *America's Climate Choices.* The National Academies Press. Washington, DC: www.nap.edu/catalog.php?record_id=12781

[11] Pew Center on Global Climate Change. (2011). www.pewclimate.org/what_s_being_done/in_ the_states/adaptation_map.cfm

[12] Kaufman, L. (2011). *A City Prepares for a Warm Long-Term Forecast.* The New York Times. www.nytimes.com/2011/05/23/science/earth/23adaptation.html?pagewanted=1

[13] CERES. (2010). *Investors Achieve Record Results on Climate Change. Boston.* www.ceres. org/incr/news/climate-resolutions-2010.

[14] UK Trade and Investment and The Economist Intelligence Unit. (March 2011). *Adapting to an Uncertain Climate: A World of Commercial Opportunities.* London, UK. Link: www.ukti. gov.uk/uktihome/item/128100.html.

[15] U.S. Army Corps of Engineers. (2011). *Procedures to Evaluate Sea Level Change Impacts, Responses, and Adaptation - Engineering Technical Letter:* www.corpsclimate.us/etl.cfm and *Water Resource Policies and Authorities Incorporating Sea-Level Change Considerations in Civil Works Programs:* 140.194.76.129/publications/eng-circulars/ec1 165-2-21 1/entire.pdf

[16] U.S. Conference of Mayors. (2011). *Clean Energy Solutions for America's Cities: A summary of survey results prepared by GlobeScan Incorporated and sponsored by Siemens:* www.usmayors.org/cleanenergy/report.pdf

[17] Multihazard Mitigation Council. (2005). *Natural Hazard Mitigation Saves: An Independent Study to Assess the Future Savings from Mitigation Activities.* National Institute of Building Sciences, Washington, DC: www.nibs.org/client/assets/files/mmc/Part1_final.pdf

[18] USGCRP. (2009). *Global Climate Change Impacts in the United States.* www.globalchange.gov/publications/reports

[19] USGCRP. (2009). *Global Climate Change Impacts in the United States.* www.globalchange.gov/publications/reports

[20] USGCRP. (2009). *Global Climate Change Impacts in the United States.* www.globalchange.gov/publications/reports

[21] USGCRP. (2009). *Global Climate Change Impacts in the United States.* www.globalchange.gov/publications/reports

[22] NOAA. (2011). *Spring 2011 U.S. Climate Extremes. National Climatic Data Center.* www.ncdc.noaa.gov/special-reports/2011-springextremes/index.php#flooding

[23] National Research Council. (2010). *America's Climate Choices: Panel on Informing an Effective Response to Climate Change.* www.americasclimatechoices.org/panelinforming.shtml

[24] Extension Disaster Education Network (EDEN). (2011). *Reducing the Impact of Disasters Through Education.* www.eden.lsu.edu/Pages/default.aspx

[25] USGS. (2011). LandSat. glovis.usgs.gov/

[26] NOAA. (2011). *U.S. Monthly Climate Normals.* www.ncdc.noaa.gov/oa/climate/normals/us normals.html

[27] NASA. (2011). *Power Of Worldwide Energy Resources.* www.power.larc.nasa.gov/

[28] USGCRP. (2009). *Global Climate Change Impacts in the United States.* www.globalchange.gov/publications/reports

[29] Federal Interagency Panel on Climate Change and Water Data and Information. (2011). *Report to Congress: Strengthening the Scientific Understanding of Climate Change Impacts on Freshwater Resources of the United States.* www.doi.gov/news/pressreleases/loader.cfm?csModule=security/getfile&pageid=260567

[30] U.S. Department of Interior. (2011). *Reclamation SECURE Water Act Section 9503(c) — Reclamation Climate Change and Water, Report to Congress.* www.usbr.gov/climate/SECURE/docs/SECUREWaterReport.pdf

[31] USGCRP. (2009). *Global Climate Change Impacts in the United States.* www.globalchange.gov/publications/reports

[32] National Research Council. (2010). *Ocean Acidification: A National Strategy to Meet the Challenges of a Changing Ocean.* www.nap.edu/catalog.php?record_id=12904

[33] U.S. Environmental Protection Agency. (2011). *Climate Ready Estuaries.* www.epa.gov/cre

[34] USGCRP. (2009). *Global Climate Change Impacts in the United States.* www.globalchange.gov/publications/reports

[35] USGCRP. (2009). *Global Climate Change Impacts in the United States.* www.globalchange.gov/publications/reports

[36] U.S. Fish and Wildlife Service. *National Fish, Wildlife, and Plants Climate Adaptation Strategy.* www.wildlifeadaptationstrategy.gov

[37] Glick, P., Stein, B.A., and Edelson, N.A. ed. (2011). *Scanning the Conservation Horizon: A Guide to Climate Change Vulnerability Assessment.* National Wildlife Federation, Washington D.C.

INDEX